The Art of Teaching Primary School Science

The long-awaited second edition of *The Art of Teaching Primary School Science* has evolved to meet the demands of schools in our rapidly changing society. Recognising that children have an innate curiosity about the natural world means that teaching primary school science is both rewarding and critical to their futures. The focus of the chapters reflects the deep expertise in curriculum and pedagogy of the chapter authors. Included are chapters on the nature (wonder) of science and how children learn as well as the nuts and bolts of teaching: planning, pedagogy and assessment. In addressing the teacher education AITSL professional standards for teaching, there are chapters on digital pedagogies, differentiation and advanced pedagogies such as problem-based learning. Finally, there is a section on STEM education that explains how an integrated approach can be planned, taught and assessed.

This book is both accessible to all preservice and practising teachers and up-to-date in providing the right mix of theoretical and practical knowledge expected of this generation of primary school teachers. Teacher educators worldwide will find this an essential resource.

Vaille Dawson is a Professor of Science Education in the Graduate School of Education at the University of Western Australia in Perth where she conducts educational research in science classrooms, supervises doctoral and masters students and teaches preservice secondary science education. Originally a medical researcher and then a science teacher, she has conducted science education research at the secondary and tertiary levels in Australia, Indonesia and India for over 20 years. Her research interests include scientific literacy, teacher education, argumentation and decision-making, critical thinking, socioscientific issues and teaching in disadvantaged schools. In addition to publishing five teacher education textbooks for primary and secondary school science, she has published multiple book chapters and peer-reviewed papers. She is Fellow of the Royal Society of Biology, an Honorary Senior Research Associate at University College London and a Senior Fellow of the Higher Education Academy. She is passionate about ensuring that all young people have access to a quality science education, regardless of background.

Grady Venville is a Deputy Vice-Chancellor (Academic) at the Australian National University in Canberra where she holds responsibility for the establishment and satisfaction of academic standards at ANU, including the delivery of an exceptional educational and student experience. Grady's career highlights have included a postdoctoral appointment at King's College London; being appointed the inaugural Professor of Science Education in 2007, and Dean of Coursework Studies in 2013, at the University of Western Australia; and a three-year appointment to the Australian Research Council College of Experts. Professor Venville's research in science education focuses on conceptual development, curriculum integration and cognitive acceleration. Grady has made a lifelong commitment to teaching and education. A central belief underpinning everything she does is that high-quality education is critical not only for human development but also for a healthy and peaceful society.

The Art of Teaching Primary School Science

Second Edition

Edited by
Vaille Dawson and Grady Venville

LONDON AND NEW YORK

Second edition published 2022
by Routledge
2 Park Square, Milton Park, Abingdon, Oxon, OX14 4RN

and by Routledge
605 Third Avenue, New York, NY 10158

Routledge is an imprint of the Taylor & Francis Group, an informa business

First edition published by Routledge 2007

British Library Cataloguing-in-Publication Data
A catalogue record for this book is available from the British Library

Library of Congress Cataloging-in-Publication Data
A catalog record has been requested for this book

ISBN: 978-1-032-00345-0 (hbk)
ISBN: 978-1-760-87812-2 (pbk)
ISBN: 978-1-003-17374-8 (ebk)

Typeset in Adobe Caslon Pro
by KnowledgeWorks Global Ltd.

Access the support material: http://www.routledge.com/9781760878122

We dedicate this book to our friend and colleague,
the late Dr Jenny Donovan.

Contents

FIGURES

TABLES

SNAPSHOTS

PREFACE

Congratulations on your decision to become a primary school teacher. Teaching is a noble and meaningful profession and you have chosen well. We anticipate with optimism that you will find joy and fulfilment through your teaching career.

With humanity facing global challenges such as overpopulation and climate change, science teaching has never been more important. In this era, the term *alternative truth* has become overused and reflects a disregard for scientific knowledge and process. As a primary school teacher, you have the opportunity to provide for your students an exceptional education in science. You have the great responsibility to teach your students the value of scepticism, evidence and critical thinking.

In this second edition of the *Art of Teaching Primary School Science*, it has been our great pleasure to work with our exceptional chapter authors, all experienced academics in university teacher education. They have interpreted the complexities of the educational research literature for your benefit and we present it to you in a succinct and easily read single volume. For beginning teachers, we have grounded the theory in ample motivating examples, so you will develop an understanding of what the theory means in the reality of the primary school classroom. For more experienced colleagues, we trust you will find much in this book that helps you to refresh your theoretical knowledge and affirms the basis on which you make classroom-based decisions.

The book is divided into three sections. The first section focuses on how people, especially children, learn. This important section explores the nature of science, contemporary theories of knowledge construction and notions of alternative conceptions and conceptual change. We include many authentic classroom snapshots and practical examples so that you can apply your developing theoretical understandings to real-life classroom situations.

The second section focuses on the practicalities of classroom-based teaching including curriculum, planning, teaching strategies and assessment. These chapters collectively comprise an analysis of what we refer to as *pedagogy*. We include a whole chapter on digital pedagogies for the primary school classroom to reflect the changing ways that we learn and teach in the digital world.

The third and final section of the book focuses on teaching and learning science as part of STEM. Primary school teachers in Australia are developing a strong tradition and great expertise in the integrated teaching of subjects including science, technology, engineering and mathematics that engages and motivates students through real-world problem-solving. We have included this section to encourage and enable you to become part of the STEM teaching tradition and to excite your students through less traditional classroom activities.

CONTRIBUTORS

Dr John Cripps Clark teaches science and technology education and science communication at Deakin University. He has taught science and mathematics in primary schools, secondary schools and universities in Victoria and New South Wales and has researched STEM education in schools across Australia and Vanuatu. John, with his Deakin colleagues, has delivered professional development to teachers through the Victorian government-funded Successful Students—STEM program and STEM Catalysts. He currently uses cultural–historical activity theory in research involving off-campus students, professional experience, school gardens and science games.

Dr Vaille Dawson is a Professor of Science Education in the Graduate School of Education at The University of Western Australia, where she teaches preservice secondary-science education and conducts classroom-based research. She was previously a medical researcher and secondary-science teacher. Her research interests include scientific literacy, preservice teacher education, and argumentation and decision-making with relation to socioscientific issues. In 2013, she was made a Fellow of the Royal Society of Biology (United Kingdom) for her service to biology education.

Dr Jennifer Donovan (posthumous) was a science educator with many years of experience teaching secondary-school science and a variety of tertiary science and science education courses. Jenny was a Lecturer in

Education at the University of Southern Queensland. Her research interests focused on improving primary science education in terms of what children learn about genes and DNA from the mass media and the surprising capacity of primary children to learn about atomic theory.

Dr Carole Haeusler is a Lecturer in Science Education in the School of Education at the University of Southern Queensland. Her research interests focus on primary-aged children's cognition of abstract concepts in science. She has published articles on children's understanding of atoms, subatomic particles and molecules and their capacity to apply these concepts to everyday phenomena.

Dr Senka Henderson is a Science Educator at the Queensland University of Technology, Brisbane. She teaches both primary and secondary science curriculum, pedagogy and assessment units across both undergraduate and postgraduate courses. Her research focuses on exploring the emotions of preservice science teachers in university settings and students in secondary school science classrooms. She has been involved in other projects related to context-based science education and mindfulness.

Dr Linda Hobbs is an Associate Professor of Education (Science Education) at Deakin University. She has designed, implemented and evaluated professional learning for school teachers for over ten years. She currently leads the evaluation of the Victorian Tech Schools Initiative. She has also led a number of projects investigating out-of-field teaching. Her research into out-of-field teaching, and teacher and school change materials developed as part of her STEM professional learning programs, have been applied to a range of contexts and other programs for primary and secondary school teachers.

Dr Christine Howitt is an Associate Professor in the Graduate School of Education at the University of Western Australia. Her research interests focus on young children's science learning, science identity, learning in informal contexts, participatory research, rights of the child, early childhood STEM education and 21st-century learning spaces. Christine has won various teaching excellence awards at the university, state and national levels for her innovative and engaging teaching in science education.

Dr Matthew Kearney is an Associate Professor in the Faculty of Arts and Social Sciences at the University of Technology Sydney (UTS). His research interests are in technology-enhanced learning and focus on how digital technologies can be used in pedagogically transformational ways in school education and teacher education. He has published numerous papers in the field of digital learning in science education. He is discipline leader of Initial Teacher Education in the School of International Studies and Education, UTS.

Dr David Lloyd is an Adjunct Researcher at the University of South Australia. His interests are futures, environmental education and eco-socially just communities. He has taught in both country and city secondary schools, and science and environmental education at the University of South Australia. He has received the SASTA 2011 Medal for outstanding service to science education, the RACI Chemex Award for contributions to chemistry and the Carrick Institute award for learning and teaching in higher education.

Dr Reece Mills is a Researcher and Lecturer in Primary Science Education at the Queensland University of Technology (QUT), Brisbane, Australia. He teaches a range of science curriculum and pedagogy units, including science specialisation units. Reece's research, in part, explores preservice and in-service teachers' attitudes and intention towards teaching science.

Dr Catherine Milne is a Professor and Chair of the Department of Teaching and Learning at New York University. Her research interests include the role of material culture, sociocultural theories and history of science in science education; author of *The Invention of Science: Why History of Science Matters for the Classroom* (2011) and co-editor of *Material Practice and Materiality: Too Long Ignored in Science Education (2019)*. An AAAS Fellow, she is co-Editor-in-Chief for *Cultural Studies of Science Education*.

Dr Wendy Nielsen is an Associate Professor of Science Education at the University of Wollongong (UOW). Her research interests include digital explanations, multimodalities and how science knowledge develops, preservice science teacher education, professional learning for supervision and doctoral pedagogy. She has been an academic at UOW since graduate studies at the University of British Columbia that followed a successful career as a secondary school science and mathematics teacher in Canada.

Dr Kathryn Paige is a Senior Lecturer in Science and Mathematics Education at the University of South Australia. She taught for 17 years in primary classrooms in a range of rural and inner city schools, in both Australia and the United Kingdom, and has been engaged in science teacher education for the last 20 years. Kathryn's research interests include transdisciplinary STEM, eco-justice, culturally responsive pedagogy and place-based education. She has co-authored two books, *Intergenerational Education for Adolescents Towards Liveable Futures* and *One Pencil to Share: Inspirational Teacher Stories from the Eastern Cape, South Africa.*

Dr Debra Panizzon is an Adjunct Associate Professor at Monash University and a research analyst for the Teachers Registration Board of South Australia. Her research interests include STEM policy, assessment in science and mathematics education, conceptual development and growth, and rural education. As a highly experienced science-education academic, she has worked with both primary and secondary preservice teachers, with much of her research involving partnerships with science and mathematics teachers.

Dr Kimberley Pressick-Kilborn is a Senior Lecturer in the School of International Studies and Education at the University of Technology Sydney, Australia. Her research focuses on innovative pedagogies in primary science education and how students' interest develops in science learning contexts. Kimberley started her career as a primary teacher in New South Wales and her classroom-based doctoral research was recognised through the *Beth Southwell Award for an Outstanding Educational Thesis* from the New South Wales Institute for Educational Research.

Dr Pauline Roberts is a Senior Lecturer and Researcher in Early Childhood Studies at Edith Cowan University (ECU) in Perth, Western Australia. Pauline has taught across the education sector in early childhood, primary and tertiary settings both in New South Wales and Western Australia, in a range of curriculum and content areas. Currently, the focus of her teaching and research is science, technology and STEM for early childhood, in particular educator perceptions of science for young children.

Dr Rachel Sheffield is an Associate Professor in the School of Education at Curtin University in Perth. She researches and publishes in science, STEM education and professional identity and is currently exploring the transversal competencies and their role in STEM. Her research and grants in STEM education have seen her travel to India, Indonesia and Malaysia supporting preservice teachers and primary students to develop expertise in STEM content and 21st-century skills.

Dr Vicki Thorpe is a Lecturer in Education at Australian Catholic University, Brisbane. Vicki's teaching and research interests include educational psychology, teacher professional practice, teaching and managing learning environments and catering to diversity. As a curriculum leader, Vicki has worked to support teachers in many projects and innovations including peer coaching and mentoring to improve pedagogical practice.

Dr Grady Venville is a Professor of Science Education and Deputy Vice-Chancellor (Academic) at the Australian National University. She is responsible for teaching- and learning-related strategy across the university. Grady's research focuses on conceptual development, curriculum integration and cognitive acceleration.

Dr Kimberley Wilson is a Lecturer in Science Education at Australian Catholic University, Brisbane. Kimberley's teaching and research incorporates science education, culturally responsive pedagogy and supporting students and teachers working in disadvantaged communities. She has produced a variety of publications on these topics, with a focus on responsive and flexible pedagogical approaches.

PART I

UNDERSTANDING THE ART OF TEACHING PRIMARY SCHOOL SCIENCE

1

ENGAGING LEARNERS IN THE WONDER OF SCIENCE

Catherine Milne

Goals

The goals for this chapter are to support you to:

- Have some fun learning about science
- Understand the role of practices, such as observing, in the doing and knowing of science
- Understand that theories and laws, which form the basis of scientific explanations, are creative constructions that are always limited by data

Australian Professional Standards for Teachers—Graduate Level:

- Standard 1: Know students and how they learn (Focus area 1.2)
- Standard 2: Know the content and how to teach it (Focus areas 2.1, 2.4)

Introduction

So many people in science and science education talk about the wonder of science and yet fail to engage learners in the joy and wonder of science. At the same time, learners are rarely placed in the role of science makers and this often means that they do not see science as part of their lives and identity. For me, your mission as educators of science is to ensure that your learners have the chance to do both.

Across the world, and in Australia, there is value in acknowledging the powerful and productive systematic knowledge systems used by learners from all kinds of cultural backgrounds in their everyday lives. By *systematic* knowledge I mean 'a collection of understandings that is organised in some way' (Milne, 2011, p. 8). I hope you will agree that the knowledge systems I explore in this chapter, Eurocentric science and Australian Indigenous knowledge systems, fulfil those requirements.

The practices that matter

You may wonder why I want to focus this chapter on practices. How would you define a scientific practice? In this chapter, you will have lots of opportunities to use various practices that help us to wonder about the world and understand science. Susan Hekman provides a useful definition of practice as, 'human activity centrally organised around shared practical understandings' (2010, p. 13). So, how can we use this definition? Consider the following two descriptions. Which one explicitly involves the practice of observing?

1. You are out for a run and you start to feel tiny drops of water hitting your arms. You say to yourself, 'It's raining!'
2. You stand at the kitchen sink washing your breakfast dishes.

Did you select description number one? How does this example fit with Hekman's definition of practice and now our definition of a practice? Let's think this through. Your body has senses, such as seeing, hearing, smelling, touching and tasting, that are activated as you experience the material world and you feel drops of water on your skin. You make a knowledge claim or inference, 'It's raining!' So, you engaged in two practices, didn't you? You observed the drops and you inferred that it was raining. Observing and inferring constitute shared practical understandings.

Consider a practice like *observing*. Humans do it, but they can only do it if they engage with the material world in some way. Practices, like observing, need to be taught and learned. Of course, science educators have always known this because, in the case of observing, use is made of activities that encourage students to actively observe, like doing a laboratory activity. In order to be an observer, learners are encouraged to use their senses to make knowledge claims that form the basis of facts (see also Milne, 2011, 2020).

I am making an argument here that observing is an important practice for school science and should be given more time. If you look at the Australian science curriculum, it is stated that, 'From Foundation to Year 2, students learn that observations can be organised to reveal patterns' (Australian Curriculum, Assessment and Reporting Authority [ACARA], 2020, np). However, the practice of observing is not explored in any great depth and the ability to observe seems to be taken for granted. I challenge you to consider the argument that, as a practice, observing forms the basis of all forms of systematic knowledge, including Eurocentric science and Indigenous knowledge.

Historically, it is from observing that facts emerge. As far back as 2400 years ago Greek philosopher, Aristotle (384–322 BCE), argued in his book, *On the Generation of Animals,* that observing provided the facts needed for the development and support of theory (Milne, 2020).

An example of Indigenous systematic knowledge that comes to mind is fire-stick farming or anthropogenic fire management (Bird et al., 2008; Jones, 1969). Rebecca Bliege Bird and her colleagues reported on how informed burning off by Martu Aboriginal people in the Western Desert of Western Australia served, over time, to create a landscape of greater plant and animal diversity. Rhys Jones (1969) argued in his paper for the Australian Natural History Museum that exploration of the literature of ethnographic studies would confirm that systematic burning was a universal strategy used by Aboriginal groups all over Australia to farm the natural environment. In response to the devastating bush fires that plague contemporary Australia, a result of Eurocentric approaches to land management and climate change, there have been calls in Australia for a national approach to the use of this strategy. Let's explore the relationship between practices, science and fire-stick farming a little more through Snapshot 1.1.

Did you note in Snapshot 1.1 how important the practice of observing was for deciding the time to burn? For me, everyday observing is a fundamental practice that forms the basis for all forms of systematic knowledge. Was this one of the practices you noted? Two other practices that you might have mentioned are *communicating* and *collaborating* because if you are going to set up a fire sequence, you need to communicate with

SNAPSHOT 1.1: *A skill that fire-stick farming and science both value*

Bliege Bird and her colleagues (2008) describe the sequence of the described relationship between the Martu Aboriginal people of the Western Desert in Western Australia and *Triodia* species of spinifex, a hammock forming bunch grass. Observe the image of spinifex. How many different species of *Triodia* can you find in Figure 1.1? In this case, what practice are you using?

As the Martu describe it, they focus on the succession of plants and how they use *cold* burning to manage the environment in that part of Australia. The stages are shown as follows.

As you follow this sequence what practices would you say are used by the Martu people as they decide when it is time to burn?

Figure 1.1 *Triodia* spinifex.
(Creative Commons. Hesparian. https://commons.wikimedia.org/wiki/File:Triodia_hummock_grass-land.jpg)

everyone else involved and everyone needs to collaborate to achieve the best outcomes. Bird and her colleagues (2008) argued that fire-stick farming is a form of ecological management that requires planning and organisation to achieve the synchronised group action. These practices are also emphasised by the Indigenous organisation, North Australian Indigenous Land and Sea Management Alliance (NAILSM) (3 Hand Studios and NAILSM, 2014) in their video of fire-stick farming called *Savanna Burning*. This video also highlights the need for collaboration between two forms of systematic knowledge: Western science and Indigenous knowledge, in order to protect the land of Australia.

These practices, observing, engagement with everyday experiences, communication and collaboration, are fundamental practices for the development of any form of systematic knowledge. They also should be the basis for science education because students should be taught in school to value their capacity to make thoughtful and powerful observations. These observations form the basis for other practices and skills that are important for science, such as questioning, making claims, conducting investigations, generating data and making arguments or explanations. Unfortunately, too often in school science, the focus is on students rote learning or confirming an expected outcome from an experiment, rather than observing the world and using those observations to wonder and build knowledge.

Everyday observing and engagement

Martin Wagenschein, a German science educator from the 1950s, argued that learning concepts alone is the wrong way to go about learning science. According to Wagenschein (1983/2008), understanding only comes from engaging with the material and living world. Let's go back to our rain example, you go outside and drops of water fall from the sky on to your body. You think to yourself, 'It's raining!' With this experience, you have created a phenomenon of raining from the interaction between your body and the water falling from the sky. But this phenomenon would never have been created if you had not experienced the world. Of course, a few other things also have to happen, don't they? You have to observe that water is falling from the sky and understand that this phenomenon belongs to the concept of rain, that is, drops of water falling from the sky. Experiences like this, engagement with the natural world, are the basis of how science historically emerged as a discipline and is how we should teach science.

SNAPSHOT 1.2: Using different senses for observation

How do children make observations and knowledge claims, using their senses? Or how do you for that matter? Try this. Go outside and sit somewhere like a park on a lovely warm sunny day. For two minutes observe as many things as you can and then at the end write down as many of the observations you made as you can remember. Now close your eyes and observe for two minutes and then write down as many things as you can remember. Now compare the lists you made. What do you observe about your two lists?

Purposeful observing and communication to make a claim or ask a question

Say you said to a friend something like, 'That lemon is really sour'. How are you able to make such a knowledge claim and what information is communicated with that statement? I would assume that you cut a lemon and tasted it by placing your tongue on the cut surface. The claim that the lemon is sour implies your expectation that anyone within hearing distance of your statement will share your understanding of the meaning of the term, *sour*. But if you were working with young people, perhaps you could check the various words which they use to describe their observation of the taste of a lemon.

You might notice that observing with your eyes closed brings to the fore lots of observations you did not make with your eyes open. For example, following Snapshot 1.2, some observers I have worked with reported hearing the leaves of the trees rustling, which is something they only noticed with their eyes closed. Each person, you, me, a child, makes observations all the time, and as educators we have a responsibility to value those observations as purposeful observing. However, much of our everyday observing is not purposeful.

Engagement, asking questions and making explanations

Activities, such as that captured in Snapshot 1.3, are designed to start supporting learners to value their abilities to make observations of the everyday world and to start to be more mindful of the world around them. Observing also provides an experience for asking questions and

---

SNAPSHOT 1.3: *Purposeful observing*

Have you seen a lighted candle? Perhaps at a birthday celebration? I would like you to draw a coloured diagram of your memory of the appearance of a lighted candle and include the flame. If you have a birthday candle light it and compare and contrast the two, your diagram and your observations of a lighted candle. Did you find that this experience initiated some questions beyond your concern that you had looked at lots of lighted candles but never really observed one?

---

making claims. Consider the following activity. Students had added table salt crystals to water and observed that the crystals seemed to disappear. I asked them, 'Where did the salt go?' One of the students responded, 'It dissolved'. So, I responded to the class, 'What does that mean? What do we mean when we say, "The salt dissolved?"' They responded, 'It disappeared'. This exchange established a space for us to ask a *why* question, 'Why did the salt disappear?' So not only are we asking 'What did you observe', we also open up a space to ask questions, such as why did that happen?

Note that what initiated this conversation and created the space for a *why* question was the practice of observing and the valuing of those observations. *Why* questions are not questions that can be explored by an experiment but they are questions that are looking for explanations (Milne, 2008). Historically, explanations initiated scientific theories. The relationship between observing, based on deep engagement with the world, and proposing an explanation, is the basis of science as a discipline. Experiences provide a context for explanations; experiences create a need to know. Without experiences, when asked why they are learning about something like gravity or the rock cycle or atoms, children often say that they don't know, but they just learn it.

Let's explore further: scientific theory and the case of the disappearing salt

The world should be exciting for young learners. Too often educators do not endorse wonder or wondering. As a consequence, young learners also do not value what they observe. When I asked the students 'Where did the salt go?' I was really following up on their observation that the salt seemed to disappear, which was the mystery. Salt is a collection of crystals. It is solid. Why should it disappear when it is placed in water? Such observations are wonderful for also bringing in questions that relate to what is needed for humans to *see* things and how the container, salt and water are a system, of a solid (table salt), a liquid (water) and a container that holds them both. One thing about science is that it seeks to be rational, that is, based on reason. Science does not draw on supernatural events to explain what happened. So, if we think of the system, the salt had to have gone somewhere within the system. The mystery is where did the salt go?

Robert Boyle (1627–1691), one of the leading natural philosophers of the 17th century, asked a similar question when noting the behaviour of air. He observed that air could be compressed and yet bounce back once the pressure had been removed (you too can compress air in a syringe). Boyle also experimented with acids, like the lemon juice you can taste, and he argued that the sour taste of acids and the behaviour of air suggested that air and acids were made of minute particles that were so small they could not be observed even with tools like microscopes. Boyle called them *corpuscles*. Others called them *atoms*. Boyle's speculation about his observations on air and acids led him to theorise the existence of tiny particles to explain the behaviour he observed. His thinking contributed to the development of a theory that science calls the *Atomic Theory*. The behaviour of salt in water can be explained by visualising water and salt made up of particles, like atoms but charged (we now call them ions). The charged salt particles separate when mixed with water particles and they seem to disappear because the particles are too small to be observed by the human eye even when aided by an instrument.

Boyle argued that in seeking to understand the world, people should base their understandings on observations and experiments. These observations became the facts that are then used to explain things. In science, those explanations then become models and theories. However, in other areas of science, observations serve other purposes. Let's explore further.

Cause and effect: an invitation to inquiry

The idea that by making a change to something, something else will happen is one of the most powerful ideas underpinning the practice of science. Imagine how powerful this idea could be. You ask yourself, if I

SNAPSHOT 1.4: Cause and effect and correlation

My sister and I are discussing novel coronavirus, SARS-CoV-2 (as named by the International Committee on Taxonomy of Viruses [ICTV]), and we joke with each other that since we have O-type blood, with respect to infection, we have some advantages over people with other blood types. Studies have shown that observational data such as that released by the genomic company, 23andMe, confirms our argument (Katsnelson, 2020). For example, these data show that there is a relationship between blood type and increased incidence of COVID-19. However, we also know that, without serious personal protective equipment (PPE), we are not keen to stand near someone diagnosed with COVID-19, the disease caused by the virus, SARS-CoV-2! Can you explain our concern?

---

change something, can I force something else to happen? This idea is the basis of experimentation in Eurocentric science, the science on which much of school science is based. Indeed, in the Australian science curriculum, *cause and effect,* finds its way into science by Year 3 as learners are asked to work with teacher guidance to test simple cause and effect relationships.

In responding to the question in Snapshot 1.4, did you think, 'Duh! Of course, the data that shows a correlation between these two variables, blood type and COVID-19 susceptibility, but we cannot say that having O-type blood (cause) causes resistance to COVID-19 (effect)'. Consider a different example, baking bread. You start with bread dough. What happens when you place it in the oven to cook? You might say, 'It rises', but we could equally say, 'It expands' because the gas in the bread expands as the bread warms up and cooks. You could say that there is a cause and effect relationship between temperature of the bread, the cause, and the volume of the bread, the effect. This relationship in gases between temperature and volume was originally explored by instrument inventor and natural philosopher, Guillaume Amontons (1663–1705), as he worked on developing a reliable air thermometer (Milne, 2020).

Consider the data I have provided next from an examination of air. In this example, I use the familiar temperature scale Celsius, even though in the scientific study of gas laws the temperature scale Kelvin is used because its zero point is absolute zero, the lowest possible temperature where there is no kinetic energy, that is, no movement of atoms.

Temperature (°C)	Volume (L)
−3	19
7	21
29	23.3
37	24
47	25

If you plot temperature (°C) against volume of air in litres (L), what do you notice?

You probably noticed what Amontons noticed, that there was a direct relationship between temperature and volume. We can express this relationship as a model, a mathematical model. In this case, it is often expressed as: $(V1/T1) = (V2/T2)$. How many different *variables*, that is, things that change, do we have in this mathematical relationship? Did you say 'Two'? If so, you are correct. What are they?

We also have a *constant*, something which does not change, and in this case that constant is pressure. In this simple system, we can explore a relationship between temperature and volume by comparing how one affects the other. By doing this, we are seeking to establish a causal relationship between these variables. We want to say that changing one variable *causes* a change in another. In this case, a change in temperature causes a change in volume and the reverse is also true, a change in volume causes a change in temperature. It might seem to you that identifying the relationship between variables is straightforward but it is not always that obvious. Also, identifying a pattern in data, like you did when you plotted the relationship between temperature and volume, is a creative act. However, once an experimenter shows the relationship, and others are able to replicate their results in different places and at different times, then the scientific community tends to accept this relationship as something that is real and it becomes something called a *Law*. This relationship between volume and temperature is now often called Guy-Lussac's Law; named after the man who showed this relationship to be true for all gases and can simply be expressed as, *gases expand when heated*.

Don't forget instruments!

Note that I mentioned that Amontons was an instrument maker? An area that is sometimes neglected in the learning and teaching of science is the role that instruments played in the development of science. For science to emerge as a global form of systematic knowledge it needed instruments that both extended the senses and were reliable, so they could be used in different places and at different times and produce consistent results. Instruments such as thermometers, barometers, telescopes, microscopes and acid–base indicators, to name a few, have a history of development that was key to the evolution of science. Yet how often are the instruments questioned when they are used to generate science observations in classrooms? For example, the development of the thermometer was key to understanding of the interrelatedness of hotness and coldness, which historically were thought to be separate phenomena (see Milne, 2019). All instruments, once formed need to be calibrated with a scale of some sort. What do I mean by a *scale* and can you explain why scales and calibration are so important? The makers of early thermometers took some time to realise that two fixed points were essential because those fixed points were the basis of calibration. Calibration allowed experimenters to be confident that the data generated from one place could be compared with data from another. These developments were essential for the emergence of science as a global form of systematic knowledge.

Cause and effect and causal explanation

As philosopher, Judea Pearl (1996) notes, we have engineering to thank for introducing the idea that objects could be used to provide causal explanations. For example, when a structure stopped working, a broken lever, or a frayed rope, or a rusted arm could be considered the cause and the effect of stopping could be explained. The engineer would say that the waterwheel stopped working (effect) because a lever had broken (cause). In science, very often we ask why that effect was observed. For example, with our previous example, we can say 'When the temperature goes up (cause), the volume goes up (effect)'. This pattern that we observe (remember the graph you made) allows us to make predictions, like 'If I heat this gas x amount, I predict it will expand y amount'. Although we can make predictions based on the pattern we have created (a Law), even if this relationship is found all over the Earth and at different times, we still do not know *why* this relationship happens. For that, we need a theory which helps us to propose a mechanism that explains the pattern.

Consider the correlation that my sister and I noted between blood types and resistance or susceptibility to the novel coronavirus. While this correlation has been widely reported, there are many possible explanations proposed to explain why the correlation was observed, including the fact that people with O-type blood already contain antibodies to A-type and B-type blood, which may make their immune systems better prepared to identify other foreign material like that from a virus (Becker, 2020). Science uses a lot of comprehensive theories including cell theory, evolution, germ theory of disease, atomic theory, gravity, quantum theory, plate tectonics and many others to explain phenomena. All these theories provide the basis for all explanations in science. For example, Florence Nightingale's (1820–1910) hospital design, which saved lots of lives, was informed by her acceptance of the miasma (bad air) theory of disease transmission (Chung, 2009). However, later in her career Nightingale accepted the germ theory of disease transmission (Chung, 2009). So, in science, theories, even ones no longer accepted like miasma theory, can encourage the development of productive explorations and provide the evidence for their own demise.

The present, the past and the future: another role for observing

While experiments are important, much of science depends on observing the natural everyday world in which we all live. Observations initiate questions and further observations, also called data, are used to answer the questions. For example, Charles Darwin did not develop his theory of evolution by doing experiments but by observing, recording and collecting materials. His extensive notebooks from the voyage of the Beagle provided him with the data he used to theorise evolution and its mechanism of natural selection (Fortner, 1992). For many sciences, especially earth science, ecology, climate science and evolutionary biology, what we can observe in the present and how we understand those observations is used to make predictions about the past and the future. Let's explore this further with Snapshot 1.5.

Of all the evidence you listed as part of the activity in Snapshot 1.5, what could be preserved by volcanic ash? What evidence could be preserved after 200 million years? Note that as you respond to these

---

SNAPSHOT 1.5: *The present is the key to the past and the future*

Go outside perhaps to a park or another open space. Think about the processes that are happening now or have happened over the past few hours and also the evidence (observations/data) that is present to support your claim for a specific process. Create a list of what is happening and how you know it is happening.

What is happening?

e.g., The clouds are moving.

How do you know? What is your evidence?

I can see they have changed position.

_____   _____

_____   _____

_____   _____

---

questions, fewer and fewer examples of evidence are preserved as more and more evidence is lost over time. We have lots of paleontologists looking for evidence of early humans but little evidence is preserved, so the record is sparse at best. In this Snapshot, you started with the present and then thought back to the past. This practice of using the present to understand the past forms the basis of many different science fields. Let's explore further. Next is a photograph I took at Lark Hill Quarry (Figure 1.2) outside of Winton in western Queensland in 2014.

If you look closely, can you see what look like footprints? What do you think made these footprints? How many different types of footprints can you find?

Finding footprints is cool but I want you to also think about what else needed to have happened for those prints to be formed in the first place. For example, what was present before the dinosaurs left their footprints? Did you say there must be mud there? If there is mud then there must have been rocks from which weathering and erosion and transport in water created the surface on which the dinosaurs ran.

For those footprints to be formed, science assumes that the conditions under which mud formed were the same 92–104 million years ago as they are today. Of course, the scientists at Lark Hill Quarry have studied

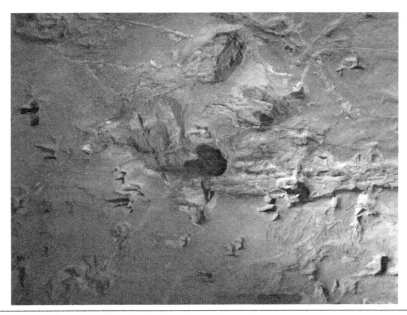

Figure 1.2 Dinosaur footprints from Lark Hill Quarry, Queensland.

this dinosaur trackway since 1984, and there are competing hypotheses or claims about the story that these prints are trying to tell us (see White, Cook and Rumbold, 2017). The idea that the present is the key to the past is based on an acceptance of the principle that all processes happening on Earth today happened in the past, although the rate at which they happened may be different. This idea that the present can be used to predict the past and the future is a fundamental key practice of science and one that deserves explicit attention in the teaching and learning of science.

Summary of key points

So often in classrooms children are presented with science concepts without any connections being made to their everyday lives. What I have tried to get you thinking about in this chapter is the need to encourage learners to see science in their lives through a focus on practices. Observing is a practice that we all do but sometimes do not value. Observing is a fundamental practice that you can use in your classroom to help your students to start to wonder about the world around them and learn about science. Engaging with the material world helps learners to make their own knowledge rather than simply being asked to accept knowledge already made by others. As educators we have a responsibility to create learning experiences in which learners are supported to make rich observations and value those observations rather than looking something up on the Internet.

Discussion questions

1.1. If we want learners to care about concepts, we need to create learning situations that make the world real. I want to leave you with some examples in Snapshot 1.6, and I want you to decide whether or not these examples are examples of science.

SNAPSHOT 1.6: Science or not science?

Example 1: Kathryn Aurora Gray, a 10-year-old girl from New Brunswick in Canada, was in the news for having just discovered a supernova using software that allowed her to make time comparisons of a specific area of the night sky near Galaxy UGC3378 which is about 240 million light years away (Jackson, 2011).

Example 2: The Yanyuwa and Garrwa people of south-west Gulf of Carpentaria in Australia developed strategies for using the fruits of cycads (Figure 1.3) for food (although they don't any more. It's a lot of work and bread made with wheat is easier). In the Yanyuwa language, the cycad is classified as wurrana or *being of authority* with economic and religious significance to the maritime environment. Use of the nut of the wurrana, also called cycad (*Cycas angulata*), as a food source constitutes a challenge because the nut, located inside the fruit, contains a neurotoxin. In order to remove the toxin, the nuts were treated by heating them on hot stones or in ashes and then pounding or grinding them into flour. Grinding stones used to grind the nuts are often found in groves of cycad palms. The flour is strained using a tool made from fronds to leach out the toxin without losing the flour. From this flour, bread called damper can be made (Bradley, 2005).

Figure 1.3 The fruits of wurrana *(Cycas angulata)* used to make flour.

Which of these examples did you locate within science and why? In making that decision, did you focus on: whether the example described was a study of nature? Whether the study was published? The procedures the researchers used to produce the knowledge? And whether the data produced had been confirmed by others? Did you focus on whether a scientific theory was central to each example? Or was there some other aspect of each example influencing your decision about whether or not it belonged to science?

Hopefully your reading of this chapter has led you to acknowledge that the answer to the challenge I gave you is not a simple one. However, each of the examples has something to say to us about the following statement: the practice of science involves working in a field of study with structures, values and ways of doing things that are used by members of the field of science to decide what should count as science. This process of testing knowledge claims through the structures, values and ways of doing things defines the field and boundaries of science.

References

3 Hand Studios and North Australian Indigenous Land and Sea Management Alliance. (2014). *Savanna burning*. Accessed October 30 2020 at: https://vimeo.com/122764056.

Australian Curriculum, Assessment and Reporting Authority (ACARA). (2020). *Australian Curriculum: Science*. Accessed June 1 2020 at: www.australiancurriculum.edu.au/f-10-curriculum/science/.

Becker, A. (2020). *Blood type may affect COVID-19 outcomes, study shows.* Accessed July 20 2020 at https://www.tmc.edu/news/2020/06/blood-type-may-affect-covid-19-outcomes-study-shows/.

Bird, B., Bird, R., Codding, D. W., Parker, B. F., & Jones, C. H., J. H. (2008). The "fire stick farming" hypothesis: Australian Aboriginal foraging strategies, biodiversity and anthropogenic fire mosaics. *Proceedings of the National Academy of Sciences of the United States of America (PNAS), 105*(39), 14796–14801.

Bradley, J. J. (2005). 'Same time poison, same time good tucker': The cycad palm in the south west gulf of Carpentaria. *Journal of Australian Studies, 29*, 119–133.

Chung, A. M. (2009). Evidence-based medicine and hospital reform: Tracing origins back to Florence Nightingale. *Plastic and Reconstructive Surgery, 125*(1), 403–409.

Fortner, R. W. (1992). Down to Earth biology: A planetary perspective for the biology curriculum. *American Biology Teacher, 54*(2), 76–79.

Jackson, N. (2011). Ten-year old girl becomes the youngest person to discover a supernova. *The Atlantic*, Accessed October 30 2020 at: https://www.theatlantic.com/technology/archive/2011/01/10-year-old-girl-becomes-youngest-person-to-discover-a-supernova/68911/.

Jones, R. (1969). Fire-stick farming. *Australian Natural History, 16*(7), 224–228.

Katsnelson, A. (2020). Genetic study suggests that people's blood type may affect their COVID-19 risk. *Chemical & Engineering News, 98*(23), 7.

Milne, C. (2008). In praise of questions: Elevating the role of questions for inquiry in secondary school science. In J. Luft, R. L. Bell, & J. Guess-Newsome (Eds.), *Science as inquiry in the secondary setting* (pp. 99–106). Washington, DC: National Science Teachers' Association.

Milne, C. (2011). *The invention of science: Why history of science matters for the classroom.* Dordrecht, The Netherlands: Sense Publishers.

Milne, C. (2019). The materiality of instruments and why it might matter to science education. In C. Milne & K. Scantlebury (Eds.), *Material practice and materiality: Too long ignored in science education?*(pp. 9–23). Dordrecht: Springer.

Milne, C. (2020). Empiricism and the factual. In M. Fludernik & M.-L. Ryan (Eds.), *Handbook of narrative factuality* (pp. 443–452). Berlin: de Gruyter.

Pearl, J. (1996). The art and science of cause and effect. In J. Pearl (Ed.), *Causality, reasoning and inference* (pp. 401–428). New York, NY: Cambridge University Press.

Wagenschein, M. (1983/2008). Save the phenomena: The primacy of unmediated experience. In M. Wagenschein (ed.), *Erinnerungen für Morgen (memories for tomorrow)* (pp. 135–153). Jan Kees Saltet and Craig Holdrege (Trans.) Accessed April 15 2008 at: https://natureinstitute.org/txt/mw/save_phenomena_full.htm.

White, M. A., Cook, A. G., & Rumbold, S. J. (2017). A methodology of theropod print replication utilising the pedal reconstruction of *Australovenator* and a simulated paleo-sediment. *PeerJ, 5*, e3427. Accessed July 21 2020 at: https://www.ncbi.nlm.nih.gov/pmc/articles/PMC5463970/pdf/peerj-05-3427.pdf.

2

UNDERSTANDING HOW CHILDREN LEARN SCIENCE

Christine Howitt

Goals

The goals for this chapter are to support you to:

- Explain the importance of children's prior knowledge in their science learning
- Describe personal, social and sociocultural constructivism as theories of learning
- Discuss the implications of constructivism for learning and teaching science
- Describe the importance of affective aspects of engaging children in science learning

Australian Professional Standards for Teachers—Graduate level:

- Standard 1: Know students and how they learn (Focus areas 1.1, 1.2)
- Standard 2: Know the content and how to teach it (Focus areas 2.1, 2.2)

Introduction

Do you believe that children come to class with valued science experiences and knowledge, or do you consider they have empty minds waiting to be filled with your science knowledge? The purpose of this chapter is to demonstrate the value of the former approach in understanding how children learn science. This chapter describes the importance of children's prior knowledge and the role of constructivism as a theory that help us to understand and improve children's learning of science. Different forms of the theory of constructivism, including personal constructivism, social constructivism and sociocultural constructivism and what they mean when applied to science teaching and learning are described and illustrated with classroom snapshots. The importance of a range of affective aspects of children's science learning is presented, including the role of motivation, engagement, beliefs and enhancing science identity.

Prior knowledge

Children's understanding of science is acquired long before they enter the classroom. From their earliest interactions with the world, children are actively trying to understand what is happening. Through play and their everyday experiences, children are developing their own ideas about how the world works. For this reason, they have been described as novice or fledgling scientists. They observe in detail what is happening, try to ascertain why it is happening and in the process develop their own personal theories or concepts. This is illustrated in Snapshot 2.1 (adapted from Blake & Howitt, 2018) where three-and-a-half-year-old Charlie brings an extensive knowledge of working with crayons through his personal experiences. This example has been deliberately selected to highlight that even young children have a wealth of experience and prior knowledge through their everyday interactions.

The scientific concept presented in Snapshot 2.1 relates to heat and the transfer of heat, which falls under Year 3 Physical Science in the Australian Curriculum (Australian Curriculum, Assessment and Reporting Authority [ACARA], 2020). Heat was caused by the friction resulting from Charlie rubbing the crayon on his hand. He correctly described this as the crayon getting *warmed up*. As the crayon warmed up, the colour could more readily be applied to the paper, making it appear bolder. As a three-and-a-half-year-old, Charlie's investigation was conducted at an emergent level; it does not require any sophisticated explanation of scientific concepts like heat, transfer of heat or friction. This Snapshot highlights Charlie's extension prior knowledge of working with crayons

SNAPSHOT 2.1: Charlie's ideas about how crayons work best

Charlie (aged three-and-a-half years) and a researcher were sitting at a table with paper and a box of mostly well-used wax crayons. Charlie drew a picture of his Nana's house and dog, commenting how some crayons did not work because, 'When they get old there's no colour left'. He demonstrated this fact with blunt crayons that had been worn down to their paper case. Charlie went on to explain that the white crayon did not work because, 'It kept its colour only for brown paper'. He proved this by producing a drawing in white crayon on brown paper. This was followed by a drawing with white crayon on white paper, with Charlie announcing, 'It's invisible!' As Charlie absentmindedly rubbed a thick orange crayon along the palm of his hand, he was asked what the crayon felt like.

Charlie: Soft. And it's not cold now.
Researcher: What was it like before?
Charlie: It's hard. And cold.
Researcher: Why isn't it cold now?
Charlie: Ah, when you draw it gets warmed up. See? In the box are cold. Touch 'em.
Researcher: So, when you draw, a crayon warms up, is that right?
Charlie: Yes, this one [a blue crayon] was writing and it's not so cold.
Researcher: I don't think I can tell the difference.
Charlie: No. Blue's not good. I don't draw dogs with blue.
Researcher: What [colour] do you draw dogs with?
Charlie: This one. It's like Nana's dog [an orange crayon]. I reckon this one is a good one. See? [He began scribbling using the orange crayon he had been holding.] Try this one. This one works better now it's been drawing. See? It's not cold.
Researcher: How do you know it works better than the orange crayon in the box?
Charlie: Because I haven't used that one yet.
To prove his point, Charlie demonstrated two orange crayons. The first crayon was *cold* and had not been used. The second crayon that he had been using was *warm* and made bolder colours.

Charlie: This one [cold crayon] is hard to draw with and this one [warm crayon] was a better colour. Look! You can do it. [Hands the warm crayon to the researcher.]

and his personal theory about warm crayons being better to draw with than cold crayons, and how hands can be used to warm crayons. This is similar to accepted science as the molecules in warm objects vibrate more than those in cold objects causing the warm object to react more readily than the cold object, and heat is transferred from hands to objects. It also highlights that teachers should never underestimate the prior knowledge that children bring to the classroom.

Prior knowledge refers to the knowledge, ideas and experiences that children bring to the classroom. Prior knowledge is important as it affects what and how students learn. Determining prior knowledge provides teachers with information on what their children know, or think they know, about a topic and ideas as to how, why and under what conditions this knowledge was formed. Prior knowledge also provides a starting point for subsequent learning. While written many years ago, Ausubel's (1968, p. iv) statement is still true today: '[t]he most important single factor influencing learning is what the learner already knows; ascertain this and teach him[her] accordingly'.

Constructivism

Constructivism is a dominant theory of learning that is relevant to the teaching and learning of science. A constructivist view of learning relates to learners constructing knowledge through their interactions with the environment (Duchesne & McMaugh, 2016). Learning is perceived as a process in which learners change their ideas by building new concepts or exchanging existing concepts based on previous learning. Thus, from a constructivist point of view, taking into consideration learners' prior knowledge is critical for enabling learning, because new understandings are built on previous conceptions or constructs. There are various forms of constructivism based around the process by which learning occurs and the knowledge that is constructed: personal constructivism, social constructivism and sociocultural constructivism.

Personal constructivism

Child developmental psychologist Jean Piaget (1896–1980) viewed learning as an evolving process that was a consequence of children interacting with the environment. Piaget considered a child progressed through a series of hierarchical developmental stages that are related to their age: sensory-motor (birth–2 years), preoperational (2–7 years), concrete operational (7–11 years) and formal operational (11–16 years and beyond) (Nolan & Raban, 2015). These developmental stages are considered to be 'upwardly expanding spirals of intellectual development' (Nolan & Raban, 2015, p. 17) where children reinterpreted their earlier ideas with new and more sophisticated concepts at a higher level. This approach emphasises that activities, ideas and new knowledge are tailored to children's current way of thinking.

The main principles of personal constructivism (Campbell, 2018) relate to:

- learning involves the learner actively constructing meaning,
- children construct meanings from their experiences and their prior knowledge, with prior knowledge assisting or hindering new learning,
- children continually seek to construct meaning about their world,
- children have the ultimate responsibility for their own learning,
- children develop their own understandings that may be different from or alternative to accepted scientific understandings (see Chapter 3 for detail on alternative conceptions).

In personal constructivism, learning takes place through active engagement with the environment where children are given many opportunities to find things out for themselves. Teachers carefully observe what children can do and say, and use that information to make decisions about their learning and how best to support their development. The fourth dot point is particularly important and can be reinterpreted as *teaching does not equal learning*. A teacher does not learn for a child. Rather, a teacher provides opportunities and support for learning. Snapshot 2.2 provides an example of personal constructivism.

SNAPSHOT 2.2: Year 1 learning about sound

As part of Year 1 Physical Sciences, the class was learning about sound. The teacher had set up four stations for the children to explore how sound travels by vibrations: feeling their throat while talking and singing, striking a drum and feeling it vibrate, exploring three different sized tuning forks and placing a vibrating tuning fork in water. Instruction for each station were given verbally and modelled by the teacher. The children were distributed across the four stations and given 10 minutes per station. Towards the end of the lesson, the class came together and the teacher asked the children what they had noticed that was common to all four activities. Many children recognised that all the objects in the different stations vibrated and described what they had observed. Some children linked this vibration to their understanding of sound.

In Snapshot 2.2, the teacher had spent time carefully choosing and setting up the materials for the different activities. The children were actively involved with the materials, although they may not have been clear about the purpose, that is, why they were doing these activities. While there was discussion between the children at each station and during the class discussion, there was limited or no scientific explanation offered by the teacher. Thus, the children were constructing knowledge for themselves which may have added to their knowledge about sound, but it may not have matched the teacher's objectives for the lesson.

The focus on the individual child in personal constructivism at the expense of the role of the teacher and the learning context, along with a lack of acknowledgement of affective elements of learning, has led to critique with the application of personal constructivism in the classroom. Also criticised has been the emphasis on children's ideas as opposed to science understanding, and the time teachers spent exploring and negotiating understandings with children as opposed to representing science (Tytler, Ferguson & White, 2019). Children can only learn a certain amount through engagement with materials—they require the assistance of an adult to diagnose prior knowledge and extend that learning in scientifically appropriate ways.

Social constructivism

Psychologist Lev Vygotsky (1896–1934) expanded Piaget's theories to include the consideration of the social settings in which learning occurred and subsequently defined the term *social constructivism*. Vygotsky also worked in child development, but his research emphasised the roles of family and community culture, the importance of personal interactions and the connection between language and cognition in children's learning (Nolan & Raban, 2015). Within the education setting, social constructivism moved away from a focus on individual understanding and towards the way a classroom environment supports learning. In social constructivism, learning is situated within the social processes (discourse, activities and contexts) of the classroom. The role of the teacher is to promote a community where knowledge is co-constructed and meanings are shared within the class (Campbell, 2018).

Vygotsky introduced the term *Zone of Proximal Development* (ZPD): 'the region between what a child is able to achieve alone and what he or she can achieve when interacting with more learned others' (Campbell, 2018, p. 60). This emphasises the importance of a *more knowledgeable other* in enhancing children's learning, whether that be through an active teacher, parent or even a more accomplished peer. 'With the support of a more knowledgeable other, the child is able to learn to do things that go beyond what they could do on their own and, therefore, go beyond their actual current developmental level' (Nolan & Raban, 2015, p. 31).

Social constructivism is characterised by collaborative or cooperative learning, discussion and listening to others' ideas. Cooperative learning is the use of small groups to achieve shared learning goals. The social interactions within cooperative learning groups have been found to enhance students' achievement, higher level reasoning skills, motivation, attitudes, self-esteem and collaborative skills (Liang & Gabel, 2005). Snapshot 2.3 provides an example of the application of the theory of social constructivism in a classroom teaching activity where collaborative learning and discourse are promoted.

Snapshot 2.3 highlights a collaborative and cooperative learning environment through the use of groups in the classroom; a learning process based on group interaction that was followed by class interaction; and discourse within those groups as the children explained, justified, debated and argued their ideas. This is an example of social constructivism in action.

SNAPSHOT 2.3: Year 3 sorting picture cards into
living and not living things

To determine her Year 3 children's prior knowledge of living and non-living, Ms Downes decided to use a card sort (Figure 2.1). She split the children into groups of five. Each group was given 20 small photographs of objects. Each child had to select one card, say what the object was, decide whether it was living or non-living and justify their decision to the rest of the group. Members of the group could agree or disagree, also providing reasons. Many of the cards, such as the photographs of animals, plants, table, car and mountain were straight forward for the children to sort with no disagreements. However, other photographs raised much discussion: fossil, seeds, the Sun and fire. The discussion of the fossil led to the group wanting to add another category of *once was living*. Two group members thought the seed was living, while the rest of the group thought it was non-living. To resolve their differences, the group decided to add a fourth category of *unsure*. Both the Sun and the fire raised considerable debate and argumentation. Some group members insisted fire was living, stating that it could move, grow, make baby fires and produce waste through ash. Others argued that it was not alive, but just appeared to be alive. After each group had sorted their cards, Ms Downes facilitated a whole class discussion where each group presented their findings and highlighted any objects they had difficulty classifying.

For any object to be classified as living, it must satisfy all seven characteristics of life: movement, respiration, sensitivity, growth, reproduction, excretion and nutrition. This is taught in Year 3 Biological Sciences in the Australian Curriculum (ACARA, 2020). Many Year 3 children do not realise that all seven characteristics must be present to classify an object as living. Some children also have difficulty recognising these characteristics in an object. For example, many children think that a plant cannot move as they relate movement to their more frequent observations of animals running, jumping or swimming.

Figure 2.1 Card sort.

Many children have limited experiences of plant movement, such as when a plant moves towards light.

Sociocultural constructivism

Vygotsky's ideas were further extended into what is known as sociocultural constructivism, where a wide range of social and cultural aspects are considered to influence learning. The sociocultural approach overlaps and extends the features of social constructivism. In social constructivism, learning is socially and culturally mediated by language and the support of more knowledgeable others and is not just limited to the classroom. Through the acquisition of language and social interactions with these more knowledgeable others, children 'acquire new knowledge and ways of thinking and behaving that reflects the culture of different communities' (Nolan & Raban, 2015, p. 29).

Learning from a sociocultural perspective includes (Campbell, 2018; Nolan & Raban, 2015):

- viewing learning as a social activity which is reflected in the classroom,
- appreciating the role of social interactions in learning,
- embracing the use of language, belief systems, specialised discourse and practices to communicate with others,
- leveraging the impact of artefacts and materials on learning,

- creating a community of learners where individuals and groups, both inside and outside of the classroom, contribute varied knowledge and expertise,
- showing an awareness of the relationship between child, family, community and culture in learning.

Regarding science, the sociocultural perspective considers that 'knowledge and learning should be seen in terms of increasing access to, and competence with, the wider community of science. Learning is seen as a process of *enculturation*, involving increasing capacity to *participate* in scientific ways of talking and acting' (Tytler, Ferguson & White, 2019, p. 42). Snapshot 2.4 describes how sociocultural constructivism is embraced in planning for teaching and learning of science in a remote Indigenous community.

Snapshot 2.4 highlights how a range of social and cultural aspects, influenced by language, can been included into the teaching and learning process. Along with the teacher, a wide range of people were included recognising the social and cultural knowledge that they bring. Both Indigenous and Western knowledge is valued in this program. There are many shared hands-on experiences with different materials where children are learning through cultural knowledge both on country and in the classroom.

Implications of constructivism for learners and teachers

Constructivism has certain implications for both learners and teachers. Children should be actively engaged in their learning, rather than passively receiving information from a teacher. Thus, they should have access to a range of activities to help them engage in and explore concepts. Learning should begin from where children are in their knowledge development journey. This implies that the first step in teaching a new science topic is to determine children's prior knowledge. For children to learn successfully, the teacher must provide opportunities to test their knowledge, ideas and beliefs. Children's ideas should be valued, and they should be given time to explore and investigate these ideas.

Teachers should respect children's varied ideas and prior knowledge. Teachers need to be aware that there can be different sets of views in a classroom regarding a particular concept: the child's view, the teacher's view and the scientific view. Teachers should provide children with activities that will engage and challenge their ideas through inquiry learning

SNAPSHOT 2.4: Learning on country: valuing both Indigenous ecological knowledge and Western science

Deslandes et al. (2019) describe a *Two-way Science Teaching and Learning Cycle* to assist the teaching and learning of science in remote Indigenous schools. The cycle involves learning Indigenous ecological knowledge and Western science through Learning on Country. Programs of work are planned with the teacher, Indigenous education workers, Elders, parents and Indigenous rangers. Topics are decided based on Aboriginal knowledge of the season, location and a focus area of cultural learning. Planning can take place in the school or on country. Students engage in a range of activities to prepare for Learning on Country. This can include determining prior knowledge, visits from Elders, becoming familiar with scientific and Aboriginal language, researching topics and learning how to use equipment. Aboriginal experts lead the Learning on Country, with Aboriginal language being used wherever possible. Photographs, videos and samples are taken to be used back in the classroom. A range of Western science activities occur alongside cultural knowledge transfer. Back in the classroom children use the knowledge and artefacts (photographs, videos, samples) of Learning on Country across a range of curriculum areas including science. Both Aboriginal language and English are used to describe processes and products. The children, school and the community then reflect on the outcomes.

or problem-based learning (see Chapters 6 and 9). Cooperative learning processes should be developed to provide opportunities for children to work together to encourage questioning and discussion, to enable and encourage children to express their own ideas and to appreciate the views of others. Teachers also need to be good listeners to better understand what and how children are thinking.

Affective aspects of learning science

Effective science learning occurs when children have experiences that engage their hands, head and heart. *Hands* refer to hands-on experiences where children are doing activities. *Head* refers to providing children with

---

SNAPSHOT 2.5: Year 5 motivation and learning about the solar system

As part of the Year 5 Earth and Space Sciences unit of work, students learnt about the Solar System. During the unit the students explored the position of the planets in the Solar System, the distance between the planets, the size of the planets and the gravity of the planets. As a final assessment, the students had to represent the Solar System at the correct size of the planets. They were encouraged to present this using any format, including a model or multimedia. Students' representations included physical moving models, physical static models, artwork, along with a range of electronic submissions. At the end of the unit, the students were asked what they liked best about this assignment. Many commented that they embraced having a choice regarding the representation, which motivated them to work with their own interests and strengths to demonstrate their science knowledge.

---

opportunities to think, discuss and be challenged in their thinking. *Heart* refers to the affective aspects that can influence children's learning. Such affective aspects are just as important as children's understanding when it comes to learning science and are considered 'opposite sides of the same coin' (Tytler, 2014, p. 86). Motivation, engagement, interest and identity are key factors in children's learning. These are generally context specific, highlighting the importance of quality teaching, the establishment of a positive and supportive learning environment and a positive teacher–children relationship (Duchesne & McMaugh, 2016). Snapshot 2.5 presents an example of how motivation, engagement and interest are related to learning in relation to the Solar System.

Science motivation

Highly motivated people 'believe that an activity process or its outcome (or both!) is worthwhile, important, interesting, or enjoyable, and that they are good at the activity or will become skilled with practice' (Patrick & Mantzicopoulos, 2015, p. 8). Highly motivated people take on challenges, put in effort, persist with a problem even after making errors and use a range of considered strategies to solve a problem (Patrick & Mantzicopoulos, 2015).

Science motivation refers to a child's level of engagement and willingness to persist in a given science activity. Children need to believe that they can perform the activity, have some control over the activity and the activity is achievable. These factors are influenced by the classroom context, the chosen activity and the effectiveness of the teaching strategy. Children also make choices about whether to become cognitively engaged with a science activity or not. If they become engaged and persist in the activity, then learning is likely to occur. If they do not become sufficiently involved, then superficial learning may occur (Campbell, 2018).

Science goal orientation and engagement

Children's goals will determine how effectively they engage with and complete a science activity. Different goals will lead to different learning: children who have a *commitment to learning* goal will have a deeper level of understanding than those who focus on a *competitive goal* of obtaining the best result and outperforming others. The deeper the level of engagement, the greater likelihood that learning will occur.

The nature of the science activity can influence children's goal orientation and engagement. The use of hands-on activities or investigations can engage children as they are learning through doing. Presenting information, problems or activities that are meaningful and relevant to children can assist them to engage with the content.

Novel and variety can also provide engagement as it introduces the unusual, unknown or unexpected. Table 2.1 presents a range of approaches that could be used to introduce novelty in a classroom. A mystery box can be used to introduce objects related to a topic. The box adds an element of the unknown, and thus engagement, as only the teachers knows what is in the box. Deliberately drawing an object incorrectly, and asking the class to identify what is wrong and how to correct it, adds unusual and unexpected elements into the classroom to enhance engagement.

Science values and interests

Children's values and interest in science can influence their learning. Children engage with tasks they find interesting, challenging and impor-

Table 2.1 Approaches that can be used to introduce novelty in the classroom (adapted from Palmer, 2012)

Novel approach	Novelty factor
Wear clothes that relate to the topic, such as Sherlock Holmes if introducing forensic science	Creates the unusual
Stop talking in the middle of a sentence and ask children to finish the sentence	Creates the unexpected
Bring an unusual object to show children or ask them to bring one into class	Creates the unusual
Ask a child to come out the front of the class to help you demonstrate something	Creates variety
Use a mystery box to introduce a range of objects related to the topic	Creates the unknown
Explain something through deliberate error and have the children correct you	Creates the unusual/ unexpected
Ask a child to teach the class something or revise a specific concept	Creates the unusual
Use popular culture to introduce a topic using videos or photographs	Creates the unexpected
Turn part of the classroom into a scene relating to the new science topic	Creates the unusual/ unexpected
Take students out of the classroom to learn or extend something	Creates the unexpected

tant to them. Children who place a high value and interest in a topic can learn more about that topic than those who place low value and interest in the topic. Children's personal interest can influence their selective attention, effort levels, willingness to persist with an activity and their final understanding. Interested children seek additional information on the topic and are more likely to engage in critical thinking. The value a child places on a topic can affect their engagement in that activity, activate their prior knowledge and support their learning through attention and persistence (Duchesne & McMaugh, 2016).

Science identity

Science identity refers to 'how children perceive whether they can do science and be successful at science, and how others perceive them at being able to do science' (Blake & Howitt, 2018, p. 125). Children's beliefs about how well they can demonstrate their understanding of science or participate in science activities in the classroom affect their *science identity*. Developing a science identity can be influenced by the opportunity to do and understand science, science classroom interactions with peers and the teacher and interacting with science resources. Children need to feel comfortable and confident in their science understandings and capabilities, especially when presented with new science information that differs to their prior knowledge. Various strategies to enhance children experiencing success include providing clear goals for lessons; providing simple and clear explanations; encouraging children to express their comments, questions and ideas; questioning children to check their understanding; praising children for effort, improvement and success; ensuring that hands-on activities work properly; circulating and providing assistance and providing flexible assessment tasks (Palmer, 2012).

Summary of key points

Children come to the science classroom with a range of knowledge about how the world works. This prior knowledge is important and is considered the starting point for science learning. The importance of constructivism as a theory of learning has been emphasised in this chapter, acknowledging that children learn through their active construction of meaning. Personal constructivism, social constructivism and sociocultural constructivism were described and critiqued, with relevant snapshots provided to highlight what these theories mean in the classroom. The importance of affective aspects of children's science learning was also presented, with an emphasis on the role of motivation, engagement, beliefs and enhancing science identity. Examples of how to enhance the affective aspects of learning were provided. The need to address the physical, cognitive and affective aspects of classroom teaching to enhance student learning highlights just how complex the teaching and learning process can be.

Discussion questions

   2.1. Discuss an instance you can recall from your own learning, or from someone else's learning where their prior knowledge affected new learning. Why is prior knowledge so important in learning?

   2.2. What is the difference between personal constructivism, social constructivism and sociocultural constructivism?

   2.3. Who can be a *more knowledgeable other* and how can they assist children's learning?

2.4. Why are affective aspects so important in learning?

2.5. Look over the novel approaches in Table 2.1 and come up with some different ideas.

References

Australian Curriculum, Assessment and Reporting Authority (ACARA). (2020). *Australian Curriculum: Science*. Retrieved July 19 2020 at https://www.australiancurriculum. edu.au/f-10-curriculum/science/.

Ausubel, D. (1968). *Educational psychology*. New York: Holt, Rinehart & Winston.

Blake, E., & Howitt, C. (2018). Enhancing young children's science identity. In C. Campbell, W. Jobling, & C. Howitt (Eds.), *Science in early childhood* (4th ed.) (pp. 124–135). Victoria, Australia: Cambridge University Press.

Campbell, C. (2018). Learning theories related to early childhood science education. In C. Campbell, W. Jobling, & C. Howitt (Eds.), *Science in early childhood* (4th ed.) (pp. 54–69). Victoria, Australia: Cambridge University Press.

Deslandes, C., Deslandes, S., Broun, D., Hugh, C., Walsh, F., Bradshaw, F., & Griffith, J. (2019). *Two-way science: An integrated learning program for Aboriginal desert schools*. Victoria, Australia: CSIRO.

Duchesne, S., & McMaugh, A. (2016). *Educational psychology for learning and teaching* (5th ed.). Victoria, Australia: Cengage.

Liang, L., & Gabel, D. (2005). Effectiveness of a constructivist approach to science instruction for prospective elementary teachers. *International Journal of Science Education, 27*(10), 1143–1162.

Nolan, A., & Raban, B. (2015). *Theories into practice*. Blairgowrie, Australia: Teaching Solutions.

Palmer, D. (2012). Student engagement in science lessons. In G. Venville & V. Dawson (Eds.), *The art of teaching science: For middle and secondary school* (2nd ed.) (pp. 159–173). Sydney, Australia: Allen and Unwin.

Patrick, H., & Mantzicopoulos, P. (2015). Young children's motivation for learning science. In K. Cabe Trundle & M. Sackes (Eds.), *Research in early childhood science* (pp. 7–34). Dordrecht, The Netherlands: Springer.

Tytler, R., Ferguson, J., & White, P. (2019). Constructivist and sociocultural theories of learning. In V. Dawson, G. Venville, & J. Donovan (Eds.), *The art of teaching science. A comprehensive guide to the teaching of secondary school science*. Sydney, Australia: Allen & Unwin.

Tytler, R. (2014). Attitudes, identity and aspirations towards science. In N. Lederman & S. Abell (Eds.). *Handbook of research in science education, Volume 2*, (pp. 82–103). New York: Routledge.

3

ADDRESSING ALTERNATIVE CONCEPTIONS IN SCIENCE

Jennifer Donovan (posthumous)
and Carole Haeusler

Goals

The goals for this chapter are to support you to:

- Understand the nature of conceptions
- Understand the nature of alternative conceptions in science and how they arise
- Use strategies that develop conceptual understanding and challenge alternative conceptions

Australian Professional Standards for Teachers—Graduate Level:

- Standard 1: Know the students and how they learn (Focus area 1.2)
- Standard 3: Plan for and implement effective teaching and learning (Focus areas 3.1, 3.2)

Introduction

Being a teacher is all about helping your students to learn. Much of the research in science education has focused on helping students to learn scientific concepts, or conceptual learning. The purpose of this chapter is to introduce you to the nature of conceptions, to understand the nature of alternative conceptions and how they arise. Most importantly, we introduce strategies that teachers can use to challenge students' alternative conceptions and help them develop conceptual understanding. Many chapters in this book expand on these ideas, they are central to teaching science.

What's a conception?

The word *conception* is used frequently in education, particularly in science education, so it is important for you as a teacher to understand what it means. A conception can roughly be defined as an individual's understanding of a particular scientific concept. For example, we often talk about a student's conception associated with scientific words such as *plant, atom, oxygen* or the *Moon*. The research literature indicates there are twin threads that contribute to the mental structures that make up a conception; one thread is about knowledge, that is, the cognitive aspects, and the second thread relates to beliefs which include feelings and attitudes. These two threads are brought to bear during the formation of the mental structures that make up a conception. For example, a 5-year-old child may have a conception of the Moon as a bright, round or crescent-shaped object that she can see in the sky. She feels happy when she sees the Moon because she thinks of a story that her Mum reads called, *The Cow that Jumped over the Moon*.

What's an alternative conception?

In science education, *scientific concepts* are considered to portray information aligned with currently accepted scientific explanations about a particular topic. Scientific concepts are evidence-based and hence rely on supporting data. When there is evidence that disproves a concept, it is no longer accepted as scientific. For example, the scientific concept that the Earth is a three-dimensional globe is well-supported by evidence, including pictures of the Earth from space. An *alternative conception* is a conception held by a person that is not aligned with current scientific thinking. An alternative conception may have a variety of sources. The child may have thought it up based on their experiences, for example, non-scientific ideas about floating and sinking can start in the baby's bath. Family members may have explained something non-scientifically, for example, parents may convey the idea that the Moon can only be seen at night. Children may take metaphorical and figurative language literally, for example, 'my car just died' must literally mean the car was alive, right? Finally, the mass media may instil alternative conceptions and we provide a specific example about how genes and DNA are portrayed in the mass media later in this chapter. To return to the example of the Earth, despite all of the scientific evidence, thousands of people the world over hold an alternative conception, that the Earth is flat. What possible evidence could those who hold this alternative conception quote to support their position? How does that compare with the evidence that supports the idea that the Earth is a globe?

Why are alternative conceptions important?

Firstly, let me explain that alternative conceptions are very common; most people have them. Yes, even you, and Carole and I must still have a few. They are surprisingly and sadly abundant in school science textbooks. They spread easily, especially if they seem outwardly plausible. Some alternative conceptions result from people holding old ideas they may have learnt at school, for example, when scientific information has changed. For example: Jupiter is a gas giant. This means it is 100% gas. Do you agree? Many people would agree with that statement and you may have learnt that at school. Not so, following several NASA missions that have probed the planet. See https://solarsystem.nasa.gov/planets/jupiter/in-depth/ for more information.

Secondly, people are called upon to make decisions about matters that depend upon scientific ideas. Politicians holding alternative conceptions about science concepts are of particular concern as their decisions can impact millions of people. The debate about climate change often demonstrates people's lack of understanding of the nature of science (see Chapter 1), that science is tentative and open to change as more evidence is acquired. This does not mean 'the scientists got it wrong first so how can we trust them now' as is often interpreted by politicians and the mass media.

What can we do about alternative conceptions?

Considerable research has occurred in the area of conceptual change, i.e., how students of all ages might be challenged to change their alternative conceptions to scientific conceptions. In summary, the educational research shows that conceptual change:

- is very difficult to do,
- is unlikely to be accomplished fully at one time,

- requires that students become dissatisfied with their current explanations/conceptions,
- relies upon the new explanation being intelligible and plausible.

Figure 3.1 represents the conceptual change process in the three boxes and highlights some of the thinking behind it in the two ovals. When you draw together students' ideas, try to keep your scientific explanation accurate, avoid too many complex words and maintain language appropriate for your group. For more information about conceptual change ideas, Gorodetsky, Keiny and Hoz (1997) is a classic paper that is easy to read and easily accessible.

SNAPSHOT 3.1: The effect of controlled burning on bushfires in different Australian states

Eastern Australia was ravaged by bushfires in the 2019–2020 summer season. These were so large, rapidly spreading and intense that they were the worst type of fires; conflagrations. They resulted in serious losses of property, and more troubling, many human lives, not to mention the deaths of a staggering one billion animals. By contrast, in Western Australia (WA), there were three major fires, all brought under control with far fewer losses. This was during temperatures of more than 40°C. So why this huge difference?

Scientific thinking has much to contribute to the way that we manage fire in Australia. Fire needs three things, a source of ignition, fuel and oxygen. One thing that humans can control is fuel. In the 1960s after a particularly awful conflagration south of Perth, the WA Government made a decision to adopt a program of controlled burns utilising knowledge of weather, fuels and biodiversity values. These are cool burns, well-monitored, and designed to reduce excess fuel. If a fire starts in those areas, it moves much more slowly due to the reduced fuel. East coast Indigenous people have likewise suggested using patterns of burning that they used which successfully controlled fires. While managing fire is a complicated and difficult matter, that some authorities have not adopted controlled burning may be seen as non-scientific decision-making which impacts millions of people's lives. This is why alternative conceptions matter.

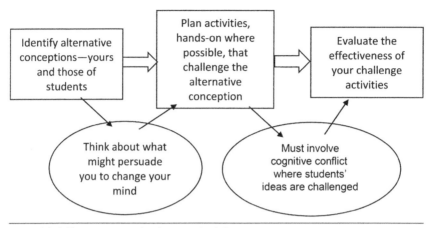

Figure 3.1 A diagram representing the conceptual change process.

One source of alternative conceptions: the mass media

As discussed above, there are a number of sources of alternative conceptions. Snapshot 3.2 explains the role of the mass media in children's learning about genes and DNA and the contribution of the mass media to alternative conceptions. A common alternative conception that appears to come from TV crime shows is that DNA only exists in certain parts of the body such as the blood, skin and fingerprints.

How do you build a conception?

'How do people build conceptions?' is a good question for teachers to think about. Here's an example to work through.

- What is your conception of a cat? Draw it, describe it, what is included, what is excluded? Do all the members of your conception of cat superficially look the same such as coat colour, length, patterns, eye colours, size? If not, how do you know they are all cats?
- What differs between your conceptions of cat and dog? Be specific, what features distinguish between them? You might find that question trickier to answer than you expected.
- How and when did you learn about cats?
- Can you be sure everyone has the same conception of cat as you? Or is this an assumption we make?

SNAPSHOT 3.2: The role of entertainment mass media in children's learning about genes and DNA

Jenny's doctoral research sought to find out how children aged 8–10 years had acquired some knowledge and alternative conceptions about genes and DNA. In the Australian Curriculum: Science, these topics are not taught until age 16. When reported, scientists and public alike *blamed* the mass media for the alternative conceptions, even in the absence of substantiating evidence. So, I decided my research would explore whether there was evidence of the involvement of the mass media and to ask children directly where they believed their ideas came from. After surveying 141 children and interviewing 62 of them from metropolitan to remote areas across three Australian states, I had my answers.

Data showed that 89% of the participating 8–10-year-old children knew of DNA, 60% knew of genes and 97% knew that humans had DNA. This fits with DNA being more featured on TV shows than are genes. The crime show effect was also seen in the nature of their knowledge. The children had minimal knowledge of the biological nature and function of DNA, only 8% being able to describe its size and shape and 6% knowing that genes are made of DNA. However, 77% related DNA to solving crime, 65% related it to identification and family relationships (e.g. identifying adopted children, unknown soldiers, establishing paternity) and 31% said disease.

The most prevalent alternative conception (51% of 62 interviewees) was that DNA is ONLY found in blood, fingerprints, skin, hair, saliva and excretions, i.e., forensic samples as shown in crime shows. Beliefs that we only have DNA to identify people for crime or family relationships, that is, it has no biological function, were held by 26%. Further, 21% believed that genes are what make us resemble our families, whereas DNA is a different thing that makes us uniquely identifiable (as a prime suspect). When asked, 80% of the 62 interviewees said they had got this knowledge from TV and most cited specific programs.

The results found clear correlations between the genetic information available from the mass media, particularly TV, and the knowledge and understandings about DNA and genes as evidenced by the children's responses. See Donovan and Venville (2014) for details.

From this example, I am hoping you can now see that a conception can be thought of in a different way—as a *category* into which we sort new information. Conceptions are:

- acquired at an early age,
- acquired with or without conscious attention,
- acquired through informal learning from a variety of sources,
- personal, i.e., not necessarily universally in agreement,
- only as accurate as the incoming information upon which they are based,
- acquired step by step, i.e., built upon and expanded over time.

Conceptual development, and the possibility of developing alternative conceptions, occurs throughout life, but in this book, we are focusing on the primary school years.

How should primary science be taught to address alternative conceptions?

Appleton (2002) noted that teachers may shape their teaching around activities that work. Although this is preferable to not allowing children to do activities, there needs to be a focus on activities that work AND build conceptual development AND challenge alternative conceptions. Is this possible? Is there a way teachers can plan to achieve this? Yes there is, and it is encapsulated in the notion of *backward design* as espoused by Wiggins and McTighe (1998). At its simplest, it is a three stage process:

1. Set learning goals (the destination),
2. Decide what evidence is needed to demonstrate the learning goals have been achieved (assessment),
3. Plan the route to the destination, that is, select resources and activities that are relevant to moving the children towards the learning goals.

Backward design is *backwards* in that teachers start at the end of the process and plan backwards to the activities. You can learn more about this in Chapter 5, the planning chapter. In science, teachers must be mindful that not all children will start from the same understanding or experience (see Chapter 2 and discussions about *prior knowledge*). The learning goals should also be flexible to avoid putting a ceiling on how far children can go. Advanced children need to be allowed to reach as high as they can. When used more flexibly, it is possible to plan science units which meet the needs of all the children in your class, will foster development of the target concept in the children's minds, will challenge alternative conceptions, and will still be a lot of fun.

Is prevention better than cure?

This is general wisdom, and given that science alternative conceptions are so persistent, Carole and I began to wonder if some science concepts are simply taught too late. By ages 13 and 14, alternative conceptions have probably existed in children's minds for more than 5 years and are firmly entrenched. Research shows children display maximum interest in science at 10 years of age. Could this be why older children do not respond well to teaching concepts such as atomic theory? Perhaps teaching these ideas in primary school would more easily change existing alternative conceptions and prevent some from forming.

Our earlier research verified a specialist science teacher's claims that he had successfully taught the big idea of atomic theory to children in Year 3/4. According to Harlen (2015), atomic theory is the number one big idea of science. This seemed to be an outrageous claim. Besides, some people expressed concern that 'it's not in the primary curriculum!' True, but observations that are in the curriculum for primary school science rely on atomic theory to explain them. For example, in Year 3, children learn about solids and liquids and the role of heat in physical changes of state.

Are you familiar with these types of dot diagrams? How would you answer the, 'What are the dots?' question from one class member?

The dots are far too big but show the same number in different arrangements. Many teachers use these diagrams (Figure 3.2). You might explain

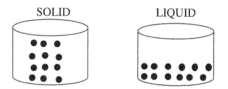

Figure 3.2 Dot diagrams commonly used to indicate differences between states of matter.

that they are *particles* but that's Year 8 work. Yet how else can you *explain* solids and liquids and what heat does?

After testing the specialist science teacher's claims in three new schools, we thoroughly agreed—he had taught them atomic theory at about Year 9 level. You can read about this work in Donovan and Haeusler (2015) and Haeusler and Donovan (2020). The children loved learning about it. They wanted to know much more than answers to *what?* questions, they wanted to know answers to much more sophisticated *how?* and *why?* questions.

Of course, the danger of not teaching an explanation like atomic theory in the younger years is that children will simply make up their own explanations. These are likely not to be scientifically accurate, so now you have more alternative conceptions to deal with later. It also robs the children of opportunities for genuine inquiry. If introduced at least to the particle level of explanation of changes of state between solids and liquids, students can pose questions such as:

1. If solids are usually denser than liquids, why do ice cubes float?
2. Liquids are often defined as pourable. But what about flour, salt, sugar? They can be poured.
3. In a narrow tube, water climbs up the side. Why?

Such questions can lead to lines of inquiry and investigations, where several activities are linked together to try to derive the answer. On one hand, children enjoy investigations and learn a lot especially when the teacher can help children to link the ideas together. On the other hand, piecemeal accumulation of facts, especially if clear links are not made to connect them to concept categories, leads to piecemeal learning. Children may be able to repeat what they have learned, but they cannot apply it to other phenomena.

The challenge to our research was 'that's OK for a specialist science teacher, can a generalist primary teacher do this?' So that became our next line of exploration. Snapshot 3.3 introduces Mila, a primary teacher who taught atomic theory.

The school was so thrilled with the results of the professional development and the outcomes of teaching atomic theory in Mila's classroom

*SNAPSHOT 3.3: A primary school teacher teaches atomic
theory in Years 3 and 4*

Mila is a keen generalist primary school teacher with a mixed class
of Years 3 and 4 children. She's not particularly into science but
does like to challenge herself with new things. Through the system network, the school invited us in to find out more about our
research. Mila participated in professional development that Carole
and I conducted at her school about teaching atomic theory to primary school students. By the end of the professional development,
Mila's hand was up as the first volunteer to be part of our research
on generalist primary school teachers teaching atomic theory.

Carole and Mila met a couple of times to aid planning, including consideration of what resources would be needed. Many of these were easily
made, such as a sheet of paper covered with glued-on sand, to demonstrate the effect that visual distance makes on the ability to see separate
particles. We visited the school early to conduct a pretest to reveal the
children's current conceptions. As in the previous schools in which we
had conducted this research, there was a lack of knowledge but relatively
few non-scientific ideas. The main one was about elements, with children saying they were 'earth, air, fire, water' and some said "the bit in the
bottom of the kettle that made the water hot". When the Periodic Table
was introduced, children were told that while these were accepted in
general language, in science, the word *element* had a precise definition as
the pure substances on the Periodic Table. So the work was mostly about
preventing the development of alternative conceptions and measuring
how much the children could learn about atomic theory.

Mila's pedagogical style was to co-construct overall learning goals
and success criteria with the children so that they (and Mila) could
ascertain whether or not they had achieved the learning goals. Children mostly worked alone or in self-formed groups to complete the
activities. Explicit teaching of scientific ideas by Mila to the children
was rare but all the more powerful when it occurred because it was a
rare occurrence. This was very different from our specialist teacher's
high school style of teaching. He would start with whole class work,
usually no more than 10–15 minutes, then have the children work on
hands-on activities with worksheets and quizzes.

of Year 3 and Year 4 (Snapshot 3.2) that the program is being expanded. There is now a drive in the school to provide useful explanations for phenomena, thereby preventing some alternative conceptions from arising. The expansion of the program of teaching atomic theory could open up possibilities of teaching the children about biological macromolecules such as carbohydrates, lipids, proteins and nucleic acids in Year 5. Would you like to see your children making models of sugars, amino acids and DNA?

As researchers, our take home message is, *Just teach it!* With two such different pedagogical styles achieving similar results, it is clear there is no *one true way* to teach atomic theory in primary school. Using the ideas as reported in our research and here, you will be rewarded with the enthusiasm of the children as their important *why?* questions are answered.

A caution: alternative conceptions are very persistent

Remember, alternative conceptions are very persistent. Do not think that 'I taught that, therefore they won't think the alternative conception any more', no matter how well you taught it. As a young teacher, I watched a research video called *A Private Universe*. When I heard the alternative conceptions from Harvard University's graduating class about the phases of the Moon over and over, it literally sent a chill through me. It made me much more aware that being an educator is not ultimately about me at all, it is all about the children, what they learn and how robust that learning is. It has stayed with me throughout my career. You can get a tiny taste at https://youtube/iMEfYLvxioc or more information at https://www.learner.org/series/a-private-universe/.

Diagnostic activities are critically important

Before you begin a topic, do some open diagnostic activities, get the children talking and see if their responses, whether they are oral, written, drawn or acted out, disclose any alternative conceptions. This information forms the bulk of your information about where the children are starting from, which is needed early in your backward design plan. If science topics typically last a term, this is best collected at the end of the preceding term so you can mull over how you can best incorporate challenges to these into your planning. Try to challenge more than once, and especially with a hands-on activity where they will be directly confronted with their own explanation not working.

Summary of key points

An important part of your job as a teacher of science is to understand the conceptions that your students have already developed about the scientific concepts that you are planning to teach. You can do that by using diagnostic activities and listening very carefully to their ideas. These ideas are called *conceptions* and very often students have conceptions that are not aligned with the accepted scientific explanations. We refer to these non-scientific ideas as *alternative conceptions* and they are very challenging for teachers of science because they are often persistent and difficult to shift from people's minds. Teaching science is about addressing alternative conceptions and helping students to develop scientific conceptions. In this chapter, we have explored ways that teaching can address alternative conceptions including using a conceptual change approach and though backward design. Our own research has demonstrated that teaching scientific concepts from an early age in age appropriate ways can prevent alternative conceptions rather than trying to cure them at a later stage in their education.

Discussion questions

3.1. A storyboard poses a question in the first frame, with others providing answers (scientific and alternative conceptions) as *spoken* by cartoon characters. How and when could this tool be useful in science teaching?

3.2. Have you identified some alternative conceptions you hold? What will you do about these?

3.3. Identify an alternative conception that you think is really important to challenge. Find or devise appropriate challenge activities that will confront children with the alternative conception not working.

References

Appleton, K. (2002). Science activities that work: Perceptions of primary school teachers. *Research in Science Education, 32*, 393–410.

Donovan, J., & Haeusler, C. (2015). Developing scientific literacy: Introducing primary aged children to atomic-molecular theory. In E. de Silva (Ed.), *Cases on research-based teaching methods in science education* (pp. 30–63). Hershey, PA: IGI Global.

Donovan, J., & Venville, G. (2014). Blood and bones: The influence of the mass media on Australian primary children's understandings of genes and DNA. *Science and Education*, *23*(2), 325–360.

Gorodetsky, M., Keiny, S., & Hoz, R. (1997). Conceptions, practice and change. *Educational Action Research*, *5*(3), 423–433.

Haeusler, C., & Donovan, J. (2020). Challenging the science curriculum paradigm: Teaching primary children atomic-molecular theory. *Research in Science Education*, *50*(1), 23–52.

Harlen, W. (2015). *Working with big ideas of science education*. Trieste, Italy: IAP.

Wiggins, G., & McTighe, J. (1998). *Understanding by design*. Upper Saddle River, NJ: Merrill Prentice Hall.

4

SCIENCE CURRICULA FOR PRIMARY SCHOOL

Vaille Dawson

Goals

The goals for this chapter are to support you to:

- Understand the importance of school science education in Australia and the role of curriculum
- Understand the purpose of science-curriculum documents and how they can inform practice at a planning level
- Be familiar with the rationale, scope and sequence of the Australian Curriculum in science, including the opportunities in the general capabilities and cross-curriculum priorities

Australian Professional Standards for Teachers—Graduate Level:

- Standard 2: Know the content and how to teach it (Focus areas 2.1, 2.3, 2.5, 2.6)
- Standard 3: Plan for and implement effective teaching and learning (Focus area 3.2)

Introduction

A quality education in science is a crucial outcome of schooling. All young people need a deep understanding of how the practice of science enables humans to make sense of the world around them. The knowledge produced by scientists allows us to solve problems and make informed, evidence-based judgements to improve our lives and those of others. For example, our understanding of science allows us to develop vaccines to treat infectious diseases, build telescopes to search the outermost parts of the universe, predict weather patterns and explain why certain chemicals react with each other in predictable ways. Many of the global problems facing humanity (for example, climate change and food, water and energy security) require science and STEM-based solutions.

There are two key purposes of school science education in Australia. The first is to provide future scientists with a firm grounding in scientific concepts, skills and attitudes so that they have the background to continue with science study beyond the compulsory years of schooling. The second—and arguably the more important purpose in primary schools—is to develop scientific literacy in all young people. Scientific literacy is the ability to use scientific knowledge and science inquiry skills (SIS) (see Chapters 1 and 6) to explain scientific phenomena and draw evidence-based conclusions about the world around them.

If we consider that our young people will need to tackle a range of future issues at local, national and global levels, then it is crucial that the primary school science curriculum includes the necessary understandings, skills and values and be implemented in an engaging and inclusive way to enable students' development as scientifically aware and literate citizens. This chapter starts by explaining what curriculum is before examining the primary school science curriculum. The aim of this chapter is to provide you with details and insights into curriculum in general, and the Australian science curriculum in particular, to assist you in being able to navigate and use curriculum documents effectively.

Before considering the primary school science curriculum, I would like to introduce you to STEM. STEM is an acronym for science, technology, engineering and mathematics that was introduced around 2001 to refer to careers in those fields. You will likely have heard this term before and may know that STEM is taught in schools. In the Australian curriculum, there are separate learning areas for Science, Mathematics and Technologies, but there is no mandated engineering or STEM curriculum. There are, however, many approaches to teaching STEM, some of which are outlined in Chapters 11 and 12.

What is curriculum?

The type of learning offered to students is dictated through curriculum documents. In Australia (and many other countries), a national curriculum has been developed that informs school leaders, teachers, students, parents and the community of what students in Australian schools should be taught in each year (Australian Curriculum, Assessment and Reporting Authority [ACARA], 2020a). The Australian curriculum is made up of eight learning areas which are Science; Mathematics; English; Humanities and Social Sciences; Health and Physical Education; Languages; The Arts; and Technologies. As well as the *content*, curriculum documents explain the *purpose* or rationale of specific learning areas as well as the *organisation* or structure. All of the learning areas have a similar organisation but differ in content and purpose.

The *purpose* of a curriculum refers to the aims or objectives and is usually linked to an overarching goal of preparing the next generation of young people to achieve their full potential, live fulfilling lives and participate fully in society. The *organisation* refers to the structure (for example, simple to complex understandings), scope (breadth of content) and sequence (order and timing of content). The purpose, organisation and content of the Australian Curriculum in science will be described in detail later in this chapter.

It is worth noting that there are different forms of curriculum, depending on the audience (Van Den Akker, 1998). For example, there is the *formal* curriculum (compulsory curriculum documents or frameworks), the *perceived* curriculum (curriculum as interpreted by teachers), the *enacted* curriculum (the teaching strategies used by teachers in the classroom), the *experiential* curriculum (learning activities experienced by students) and, finally, the *attained* curriculum (the actual learning by the students). Alignment across these various levels of curriculum does not always happen, as the things that students actually learn can be quite different from the formal curriculum. It is important for teachers to keep this factor in mind, as they are the key people responsible for interpreting and enacting the curriculum in ways that both reflect its aims and make sense for their students. In this chapter, the discussion is usually referring to the formal curriculum of Australia (ACARA, 2020a).

Using science curriculum documents

When you commence your first job as a beginning teacher, a question uppermost in your mind is likely to be, 'What do I actually teach these students?' You will most likely have developed skills about how to construct a lesson plan or sequence of lessons but might feel uncertain about exactly what content needs to be taught and where to access this information.

In some schools, especially larger ones, there may be well-documented teaching programs that set out a sequence of learning and teaching activities. Other schools may have little to draw upon. Sometimes it can be difficult to pick up another teacher's program and use it without understanding why particular outcomes, learning activities or assessments are specified. It is a bit like following a knitting pattern without having a picture of the whole garment. Who knows what the final product will look like? You need to be aware of what your students might already know from their home life and previous years of schooling and what they will need to know by the time you have finished teaching them. The most important source of information about *what* to teach, and *how* and *why*, will be *formal* curriculum documents.

Formal curriculum documents are provided to teachers by government educational jurisdictions to help them to know *what* to teach and *why*. These documents may be supported by a syllabus, assessment items, sample programs and student work samples. The curriculum documents help teachers to plan their lessons, select curriculum resources, develop learning activities and assess students' learning. Science curriculum documents provide information about the sequence, breadth and depth of science learning at each year level. Typically, scientific concepts are revisited throughout the years of schooling so that students are exposed to similar concepts in increasing complexity as they progress. Although the terminology varies, the content areas of biology, chemistry, physics and earth and space science, and SIS (for example, developing questions, designing fair tests, collecting and analysing data, constructing conclusions), nature of science and the role of science in society, are generally included in formal curriculum documents worldwide.

The *experiential* curriculum (in other words, the learning activities that students participate in) depends not only on the *formal* curriculum but also on a number of other factors, including:

- support, such as professional development, provided by the education sector (e.g., government, Catholic, independent),

- curriculum resources (e.g., designated space, equipment, books, science garden, animals) available at the school,
- ICT resources and support (e.g., laptops, iPads/tablets),
- the priority given to science compared with other learning areas in your school and state/territory,
- time allocation,
- financial budget allocated to science in the school,
- teacher expertise, experience and interest,
- teacher beliefs about how science should be taught,
- student factors, such as achievement levels, aspirations, previous science experiences and attitudes to science,
- community and parental expectations.

To summarise, *curriculum* provides big-picture information about what to teach and why, whereas *syllabus* enables the drilling down to provide greater detail about what to teach and how. Both curriculum and syllabus documents are drawn upon to inform the development of *program* outlines, which list the content to be taught and provide a learning sequence, and the creation of *lesson plans*, which provide guidance on how content is delivered on a daily basis.

The Australian Curriculum in science

The Australian Curriculum: Science is fully implemented in government schools in its intended form in six of the eight states and territories—the Australian Capital Territory, the Northern Territory, Queensland, South Australia, Tasmania and Western Australia. The science-curriculum document is available in both a paper-based and a hyperlinked web-based version. The online version has functionality that allows users to search according to their needs (for example, specifying particular year levels or strands of science).

While all states and territories have endorsed the Australian Curriculum, not all have adopted it in its entirety. The states of New South Wales and Victoria each have their own version of curriculum documents for teachers in their state jurisdictions, guided respectively by:

- the New South Wales Science and Technology K–6 Syllabus (NSW Education Standards Authority, 2020) which has students introduced to scientific and technological concepts and skills across five areas of the Living World, Material World, Physical World, Earth and Space, and Digital Technologies,

- the Victorian Curriculum F–10 (Victorian Curriculum and Assessment Authority, 2020) which has two strands, Science Understanding and Science Inquiry Skills. Science as a Human Endeavour (SHE) is a sub-strand of Science Understanding.

These curricula encompass and are largely consistent with the Australian Curriculum but have been contextualised to suit the setting. The Catholic and independent education sectors in all states and territories work in a similar way, by linking to the Australian Curriculum within their own versions in ways that make sense in terms of their ethos, communities and students' needs. When you have finished reading this chapter, it is recommended you browse the Australian Curriculum website and your state and territory equivalent to familiarise yourself with the extensive amount of material there.

For the purpose of this chapter, and given its pivotal role in curriculum development and implementation regardless of location or jurisdiction, the Australian Curriculum: Science will be the focus for the remainder of this chapter. The purpose, organisation and content of the Australian science curriculum are described next.

Purpose

The Australian science curriculum describes the rationale and aims of school science education from Foundation (the year prior to commencing Year 1) to Year 12. In the rationale, science is described as a 'dynamic, collaborative and creative human endeavour arising from our desire to make sense of our world through exploring the unknown, investigating universal mysteries, making predictions and solving problems' (ACARA, 2020a, rationale). This quote provides insights into the aims of the science curriculum to support students in becoming scientifically literate. It aims to achieve this through the provision of a strong grounding in the conceptual understandings of science as well as scientific methodologies, and the development of critical and creative thinking skills that build students' capabilities to investigate the world around them.

There are seven aims of the science curriculum across all year levels. They are:

1. an interest in and curiosity about science,
2. an understanding that science explains the living and non-living world,
3. an understanding of scientific inquiry,
4. an ability to communicate scientifically to a range of audiences,
5. an ability to solve problems and make informed, evidence-based decisions,
6. an understanding of historical and cultural contributions to science,
7. a knowledge base in biological, chemical, physical and earth and space sciences.

The way the Australian science curriculum is organised, as explored in the next section, helps to explain how these aims are realised.

Organisation

The organisation of the Australian science curriculum can initially seem confusing. Figure 4.1 provides a graphic that illustrates the organisation. The other seven learning areas have a similar organisation to science.

Strands

The curriculum is organised into three interrelated *strands*: *Science Understanding*, *Science as a Human Endeavour* and *Science Inquiry Skills*. Together, these strands describe the understandings, knowledge and skills that learners need to develop a scientific understanding of their experiences and the world. Individually, each strand has a particular purpose. *Science Understanding* (SU) focuses on the content required to address the key ideas and skills of science and is situated within appropriate contexts for the learner (for example, year level, needs and settings). *SHE* supports students in connecting with science as a way of knowing and doing and highlights the role of decision-making and problem-solving in science, but in ways that take into account ethical and socially responsible practices and implications. *SIS* enables students to develop the thinking and procedural tools needed to move towards deeper, more meaningful

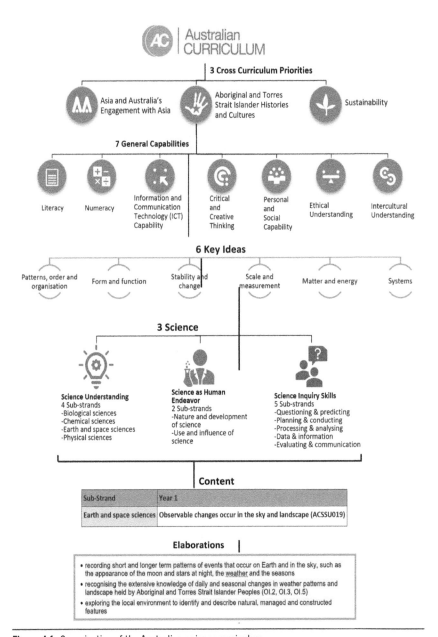

Figure 4.1 Organisation of the Australian science curriculum.

conceptual understandings of science, such as questioning, predicting, collecting and analysing data, making sense of findings and ways of communicating their ideas and understandings.

Each of these strands is further divided into *sub-strands*. SU has four sub-strands, SHE is divided across two areas and SIS has been broken down into five parts. The sub-strands are described in more detail in the content section later, but essentially they build upon each other conceptually and in complexity across the years of schooling. It is intended that the strands are taught in an integrated way. For each year of schooling, the sub-strands are described as *content descriptors* with *elaborations* to illustrate them. See Figure 4.1 which outlines the Year 1 content descriptor and three of the elaborations.

Key ideas

In addition to the strand and sub-strand structure in the Australian science curriculum, there are six *key ideas* that are fundamental to science education and bridge the strands. In particular, they highlight the important aspects of a scientific worldview and bridge understanding and knowledge dimensions across the science strands and sub-strands.

The key ideas, with a brief description of what they cover, are:

1. patterns, order and organisation—recognising patterns in the world, along with ordering and organising science phenomena using meaningful scales of measurement,
2. form and function—form refers to the characteristics of an object/organism, whereas function refers to how those characteristics impact on its use,
3. stability and change—understanding that some phenomena are stable over time, while others change,
4. scale and measurement—articulation of time and scale is important in the development of science understanding, as it provides a benchmark for comparisons,
5. matter and energy—the ability to describe observations of, and changes in phenomena using the terminology of matter and energy,
6. systems—making sense of phenomena (including predicting what will happen) by exploring, describing and analysing systems.

The key ideas are used to develop *year level descriptions.* These descriptions integrate the strands and key ideas for a particular year of schooling. For example, in reference to Figure 4.1, the Year 1 level descriptor is:

> From Foundation to Year 2, students learn that observations can be organised to reveal patterns, and that these patterns can be used to make predictions about phenomena.

In Year 1, students infer simple cause-and-effect relationships from their observations and experiences and begin to link events and phenomena with observable effects and to ask questions. They observe changes that can be large or small and happen quickly or slowly. They explore the properties of familiar objects and phenomena, identifying similarities and differences. Students begin to value counting as a means of comparing observations and are introduced to ways of organising their observations (ACARA, 2020b).

General capabilities

In examining the organisational aspects of the curriculum in greater detail, across all learning areas of the Australian Curriculum (science included), there are broad skills and behaviours that are considered important for all young people to achieve. These skills and behaviours are referred to as *general capabilities* and are embedded in the content of all curriculum areas. They are intended to provide opportunities to add richness and depth to student learning within the different key learning areas, which in this case is science. The seven general capabilities and examples of how they might be understood in reference to science learning and teaching are:

1. literacy—e.g., interpreting media articles, presenting claims, formulating predictions, using technical science vocabulary accurately and using language appropriate for the context and audience,
2. numeracy—e.g., measurement (use of formal units), representing data (tables and graphs), identifying patterns and trends in numerical data,
3. ICT competence—e.g., accessing information, representing science phenomena and using technology as a digital aid (i.e., creating animations and simulations) and for communicating science understanding,

4. critical and creative thinking—e.g., generating new or novel ideas and solutions, encouraging open-mindedness in making sense of the world and enabling active inquiry (e.g., predicting, speculating),

5. personal and social capability—e.g., taking the initiative, applying scientific knowledge to daily life, displaying curiosity, questioning and making informed decisions about issues that impact their lives,

6. ethical understanding—e.g., forming and making ethical judgements, understanding honesty in science, applying ethical guidelines and using scientific information to inform ethical decision-making processes,

7. intercultural understanding—e.g., appreciating the contribution of different cultural perspectives to science knowledge, being aware of culturally diverse ways of making sense of the world and demonstrating cultural sensitivity in relation to some areas of debate in science.

Cross-curriculum priorities

Finally, there are three *cross-curriculum priorities* that need to be included in all learning areas, including science. The inclusion of these priorities stems from the *Melbourne Declaration* (Ministerial Council on Education, Employment, Training and Youth Affairs [MCEETYA], 2008), a statement and commitment from all state and territory governments that led to a set of goals to ensure high-quality schooling for all young Australians. This included the development of a curriculum, from which the Australian Curriculum arose, which is relevant, contemporary and engaging for students. From this declaration, three key areas were identified and intended to be interwoven through the curriculum for the benefit of individuals and Australia collectively, as they draw on regional, national and global components to enrich and enliven learning. *Icons* (as in Figure 4.1) are used to indicate opportunities to develop or apply one or more of these cross-curriculum priorities as a way to enhance the learning of a particular topic or content.

The cross-curriculum priorities are:

• Aboriginal and Torres Strait Islander histories and cultures—provision of opportunities to deepen knowledge and understanding through the elements of identity and living communities by drawing on insights from three key ideas: country/place, people and culture. The elaborations for each sub-strand of the Australian science curriculum provide a specific example of how to integrate this priority,

- Asia, and Australia's engagement with Asia—building on and extending regional connectedness by developing an understanding through three key concepts: Asia and its diversity, achievement and contributions of the peoples of Asia and Asia–Australia engagement,

- Sustainability—with a focus on more sustainable patterns of living, there are three underlying conceptual areas to connect with in terms of how humans interact with each other and their environments: systems, worldviews and futures.

Recently, the new *Alice Springs (Mparntwe) Education Declaration* (Education Council, 2019) was released that emphasises that all young Australians become 'successful lifelong learners who are able to make sense of their world and think about how things have become the way they have' (p. 7).

Content

Foundation to Year 6

As identified previously in this chapter, the science curriculum from Foundation to Year 6 comprises the three interrelated strands of *Science Understanding*, *Science as a Human Endeavour* and *Science Inquiry Skills*. Each strand is further divided into sub-strands. For example, in Foundation to Year 6, *Science Understanding* is divided into four sub-strands— biological, chemical, earth and space, and physical sciences.

On the ACARA (2020a) website, for each year level from Foundation to Year 6, there is a *year level description (based on the key ideas)*, a *year achievement standard* (a statement about what students are able to demonstrate at the end of each year) and a number of annotated *work samples*. These work samples provide evidence of student learning in relation to the required achievement standard and illustrate satisfactory, above-satisfactory and below-satisfactory student achievement. This is intended to assist teachers in making judgements about the quality of their students' achievement. There are also *content descriptions* for each of the sub-strands (see Figure 4.1), which identify key conceptual understandings and knowledge. *Elaborations* associated with each content description provide further insights and examples of the content to be addressed. Although these terms may initially seem confusing, they are used consistently throughout the curriculum documents for all learning areas and will become familiar through regular use. Snapshot 4.1 illustrates how the different aspects can be considered when planning to teach.

SNAPSHOT 4.1: Using the curriculum documents and applying them in the local school context

Holly has just been appointed to her first teaching job in a small town on the coast. The school principal has given her a copy of the school plan and advised her she will have a Year 5 class. The school plan lists science and the environment as a school priority. Holly goes to the Australian Curriculum: Science website and reads the Year 5 content descriptions for the three science strands. She notes that students need to learn how to collect data and construct tables and graphs. In the biological sciences sub-strand of science understanding, students explore adaptations in living things. Holly observed that the school oval is adjacent to undeveloped wetlands and that the density and types of vegetation and insects differ under the trees, in the wetter parts and in open areas near the school oval. She subsequently discovers that the town council publishes a guide to local flora and fauna using both English and local Indigenous names. She wonders if she can enlist the support of a local Elder. Holly consults Figure 4.1 and does a brainstorm to record opportunities to embed the cross-curriculum priorities of sustainability and Aboriginal and Torres Strait Islander histories and cultures, the general capabilities of numeracy, critical and creative thinking and intercultural understanding and the key idea of form and function. She thinks she could plan a term long program with an excursion halfway through to collect data on type, number and height of plants in the wetlands. The next step is structuring her planning in a more formal way as outlined in Chapter 5.

Summary of key points

This chapter provided a summary of key features of the science curriculum documents that guide the teaching, learning and assessment of science throughout Australia. It is important to note that while the curriculum documents provide guidance for teachers, this does not guarantee effective teaching. Rather, they are a guide for the teachers and it is the teacher who interprets them. What and how we teach will inevitably be influenced by our own beliefs and values about science and pedagogy, and other factors such as the resources available, student age, school culture, ability, interest and aspirations of students and parental and community expectations.

Discussion questions

4.1. Go to the science learning area of the Australian Curriculum website (www.australiancurriculum.edu.au). Select a year level, strand, sub-strand and content descriptor. Look at the elaborations to assist you to identify three learning activities that you could use in teaching this part of the curriculum.

4.2. Consider a unit of work on heat production and transfer in Year 3 science. What opportunities might there be to integrate some of the general capabilities into this learning experience? What connections could be made to one or more of the cross-curriculum priorities?

4.3. Identify a contemporary issue in your community (for example, recycling) and investigate the ways in which it might connect with the strands and sub-strands in the Australian Curriculum: Science. How might you leverage this real-world issue to create a meaningful science-learning and teaching opportunity?

References

Australian Curriculum, Assessment and Reporting Authority (ACARA). (2020a). Accessed May 13 2020 at: https://www.australiancurriculum.edu.au/about-the-australian-curriculum/.

Australian Curriculum, Assessment and Reporting Authority (ACARA). (2020b). *Australian Curriculum: Science*. Accessed May 13 2020 at: www.australiancurriculum.edu.au/f-10-curriculum/science/.

Education Council. (2019). *Alice Springs (Mparntwe) Education Declaration*. Accessed July 11 2020 at: http://www.educationcouncil.edu.au/site/DefaultSite/filesystem/documents/Reports%20and%20publications/Alice%20Springs%20(Mparntwe)%20Education%20Declaration.pdf.

Ministerial Council on Education, Employment, Training and Youth Affairs (MCEETYA). (2008). *Melbourne Declaration on Educational Goals for Young Australians*, Carlton: Author.

NSW Education Standards Authority. (2020). Accessed June 15 2020 at: https://educationstandards.nsw.edu.au/wps/portal/nesa/k-10/learning-areas/science/science-and-technology-k-6-new-syllabus.

Van Den Akker, J. (1998). The science curriculum: Between ideals and outcomes. In B. J. Fraser & K. G. Tobin (Eds.), *International handbook of science education* (pp. 421–447). Dordrecht, The Netherlands: Kluwer.

Victorian Curriculum and Assessment Authority. (2020). Accessed June 15 2020 at: https://victoriancurriculum.vcaa.vic.edu.au/science/introduction/structure.

PART II
IMPLEMENTING THE ART OF TEACHING PRIMARY SCHOOL SCIENCE

5

PLANNING ENGAGING AND SAFE SCIENCE LESSONS

Reece Mills and Senka Henderson

Goals

The goals for this chapter are to support you to:

- Understand the importance of planning to support student learning and engagement in primary school science
- Plan primary school science units of work and lessons that use the learning theory of constructivism as a referent
- Evaluate the safety of primary school science activities

Australian Professional Standards for Teachers—Graduate Level:

- Standard 3: Plan for and implement effective teaching and learning (Focus areas 3.1, 3.2, 3.3, 3.4, 3.6)
- Standard 4: Create and maintain supportive and safe learning environments (Focus area 4.4)

Introduction

Planning in science is critical for successful science teaching because it maps out students' developing scientific understanding and ensures alignment between curriculum goals, teaching and learning activities and assessment. This mapping can occur on different time scales ranging from one lesson to an entire school year. There are lots of factors that need to be considered when planning for learning in science, including what to teach, why to teach it, the goal of the teaching and learning, how students will learn the content, how learning will be assessed, what will be reported and (after the lesson) the teacher's evaluation of the lesson. While all of these things may seem complex and may even be confusing when you are starting out as a new teacher, they will become second nature before long. This chapter will walk you through these factors and help you to develop your initial understanding of planning for successful science teaching and learning. Important ideas about planning in science will first be introduced, before three levels of planning—macro, meso and micro—are explained. Snapshots of real planning documents are used in this chapter to show you how to construct whole-school, year-level, unit and lesson plan documents.

Planning for learning in primary school science

In this section, we will introduce six important ideas that you will need to know when planning for learning in primary school science. These are:

1. *Planning based on social constructivism.* Social constructivism is a learning theory built on the premise that children co-construct with others their understanding of the world around them through linking existing and new knowledge and experiences (see Chapter 2 for more information about constructivism). This means that learning activities in primary school science ought to be learner-centred, include hands-on activities, build upon students' existing ideas and incorporate collaborative group work.

2. *Planning integrates the three strands of the Australian Curriculum: Science so they are taught together.* The *Australian Curriculum: Science* has three interrelated strands: Science Understanding, Science Inquiry Skills and Science as a Human Endeavour (see Chapter 4). Together, these three strands provide students with the knowledge and skills needed to develop a scientific view of the world. Learning outcomes from all three strands should be considered when planning in primary school science, such that students' learning is built around scientific inquiry and reflects the nature of science as a unique way of knowing and doing.

3. *Planning uses backward design.* The planning process in primary school science begins with a consideration of the desired learning outcome/s. Planning documents then lay out how teaching and learning activities, including specific teaching strategies and resources, are sequenced to guide students towards achieving these outcomes. Planning documents also clearly state what evidence of learning is collected along the way through assessment. The backward design process ensures alignment between learning outcomes, teaching and learning activities and assessment.

4. *Planning is a collaborative and public endeavour.* Planning in primary school science is often a collaborative effort, with teachers sharing ideas and responsibilities. Teachers may meet to carry out scoping and sequencing activities (what, when and how teaching and learning occurs) to ensure coherence in learning across and within year levels. Planning documents are sometimes shared with many stakeholders such as school administrators, parents and carers. This means they are public documents and ought to be well-planned, complete and accurate.

5. *Planning documents are 'living' documents that respond to students' changing interests and needs.* It is important to adjust planning documents along the way if students 'aren't getting it' or school circumstances, like assemblies or excursions, get in the way. Continuously reflecting upon and evaluating planning documents is important in terms of ensuring the currency and relevance of topics, availability of personnel and resources and the effectiveness of learning and teaching activities for promoting student engagement/motivation and achievement.

6. *Planning must be specific to a school and classroom context.* Teachers often draw upon existing teaching and learning resources to create planning documents in primary school science. While state education departments offer sample documents for planning and assessment, these are generic, one size fits all examples. It is expected that teachers carefully consider the situation and needs within their school community and adapt planning documents to suit the school context and the specific needs of the students in their classroom.

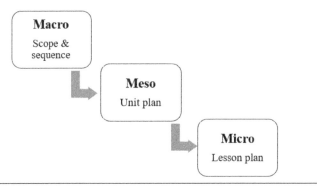

Figure 5.1 Levels of planning.

These important ideas should be applied across macro, meso and micro levels of planning (Figure 5.1). The remainder of this chapter is structured around these levels of planning. Each level has a different purpose and incorporates different information and amounts of detail. Whole-school, year-level, unit and lesson planning will be unpacked with examples in the following sections.

Macro level: whole-school and year-level planning

Whole-school planning in science is conducted to ensure children's scientific understanding develops across their formal years of schooling. There are *big ideas* (Harlen, 2015) in science that are built from Foundation Year onwards. The progression of these ideas from *smaller* to *bigger* is described by the Australian Curriculum: Science (Australian Curriculum, Assessment and Reporting Authority [ACARA], 2020), which prescribes what is taught at each year level. Whole-school and year-level planning documents ensure everyone in the school community knows *what* and *when* students are learning, and that the concepts and skills children learn in earlier years are built upon in subsequent years minimising gaps and repetition. Whole-school and year-level planning documents are generally mapped out by a senior experienced teacher or school leader, like a deputy principal or head of curriculum but may also include classroom-based teachers. This macro-level planning from Foundation Year onwards is sometimes called vertical planning. One example of a whole-school science planning document is provided in Snapshot 5.1.

Sometimes international, national, state and territory (e.g., government) and local (e.g., school) priorities are considered when planning

SNAPSHOT 5.1: An example of a whole-school science plan—or vertical planning

Terms/Year level	Foundation	Year 1	Year 2	Year 3	Year 4	Year 5	Year 6
Term 1	Needs of living things	A living adventure	Good to grow	Living and non-living	Life cycles and habitat	Survival in the environment	Life on earth
Term 2	Objects and their properties	Don't rock the boat	Mix, make and use	Melting moments	Energy at work	My place in space	Making changes
Term 3	Seasonal changes	Changes around me	Saving planet earth	Exploring space	Geology rocks!	Matter and changing states	Our changing world
Term 4	Moving objects	Exploring light and sound	Designing a toy	Heating up	A material world	Light	Energy and electricity

at the whole-school level. As outlined in Chapter 4, these priorities are determined by educational authorities like the ACARA and are written into the curriculum (e.g., General Capabilities such as literacy and numeracy). Other times they might be peripheral to the curriculum but still important agendas like STEM (science, mathematics, engineering and technology) education and careers or climate change. The school's context and culture, available resources and needs of the community must be considered when developing a school science curriculum. A school may have a current priority about environmental sustainability, for example, and this may need to be used as a context for students' learning of science or embedded in science units and lessons at a whole-school level.

A year-level plan in primary school science describes the focus topics and assessment to be implemented each term over one school year. This planning document elaborates on the whole-school plan by providing more detailed information. Snapshot 5.2 provides an example of a year-level primary science plan for Year 2 over the four terms in a school year.

Meso level: unit planning

Unit planning and lesson planning are the most common types of documents created by teachers so will be explored in-depth in this and the next section. Unit planning focuses on one specific topic or unit of work listed in the year-level plan. A unit of work is a series of science lessons where the concepts in a topic are taught as part of the science curriculum. Each lesson in a unit plan should be related to the ones that come before and after so that students' understanding of the target science concepts builds over the duration of the unit. A unit plan is the *middle picture* or meso-level document for planning to teach science in primary school classrooms. In planning a primary school science unit, the teacher needs to carefully consider and decide upon the duration and timing, learning outcomes, context, assessment, sequence of learning and the specific teaching and learning strategies. An example of a unit plan for Year 6 on the topic of electrical energy and circuits is provided in Snapshot 5.3. These tasks are now explained in more detail in the sections below as this will be an important task as you start your teaching career.

Snapshot 5.2: An example of a year-level science plan

Year 2 Science Achievement Standard (ACARA, 2020)
By the end of Year 2, students describe changes to objects, materials and living things. They identify that certain materials and resources have different uses and describe examples of where science is used in people's daily lives. Students pose and respond to questions about their experiences and predict outcomes of investigations. They use informal measurements to make and compare observations. They record and represent observations and communicate ideas in a variety of ways.

	Focus topic/s	Assessment
Term 1 Living and non-living	• Personal growth • Life stages of humans, plants and animals • Characteristics of life stages • Parents and offspring	*Storyboard—How does it grow?* • Compare life stages of two different animals • Explain characteristics of the different life stages • Present findings to other students
Term 2 Mix, make and use	• Properties of materials • Combining materials • Re-making and recycling	*Assessment booklet—Combining materials* • Investigate the combination of materials used to make an object for a particular purpose • Record and represent observations and communicate ideas
Term 3 Saving planet Earth	• Resources in the schoolyard • Water cycle and conservation • Using Earth's resources responsibly	*Create a poster—Water at home* • Identify different uses of one of Earth's resources and describe ways to conserve it • Use informal measurements to make observations
Term 4 Designing a toy	• Forces—push and pull and gravity • Strength of pushes and pulls • Shape of an object and movement • Surfaces and rolling objects	*Model building—Design a push/ pull toy* • Design a toy (decide which parts of the toy will help it move) • Choose and justify materials to construct it • Make predictions, observations and make changes to the toy design

Duration and timing

A unit of work in primary school science may span a half or full term (i.e., 5–10 weeks in length) depending on the topics to be covered and whether the unit of work integrates with other learning areas such as mathematics and technologies in a STEM unit. The volume of learning in science required over one school year is often defined by state and territory regulatory authorities and teachers work out how many hours of science learning per week must be planned. For example, in Queensland, the Department of Education specifies that in Foundation to Year 2 students must have 1 hour of science learning per week and in Year 3 to Year 6 students must have 1 hour 45 minutes of science learning per week (Queensland Department of Education, 2020). This has implications for how a unit of work is mapped out over a half or full school term.

Another consideration is the timing of primary school science lessons. It is possible to distribute the volume of learning in many different ways. As a general guide, lessons in the early primary years are shorter in duration (e.g., 30 minutes), whereas lessons in the middle and upper primary years may be longer in duration (e.g., 60 minutes). Of course, this may not always occur in one solid block of time, for example, students may collect data about light and shadows at different times of the day or collect data about the growth of plants every morning or afternoon.

Learning outcomes

The most important learning outcomes in a unit of work are identified in the Australian Curriculum: Science in the achievement standard. This describes what a student must understand and be able to do by the end of a given year level. You can see the achievement standard is included at the top of the year-level plan in Snapshots 5.2 and 5.4. From the achievement standard, teachers write more specific learning outcomes and map them to individual lessons. These may take the form of learning intentions and success criteria (what is being learnt and the evidence of learning). As part of planning for learning in primary school science, teachers must also include General Capabilities (e.g., literacy, numeracy and ICT) and Cross Curriculum Priorities (e.g., environmental sustainability, Indigenous knowledges and perspectives) in their unit plan documents. The embedding of General Capabilities and Cross Curriculum

Priorities should enhance a student's capability in the given area, while also supporting their scientific understanding.

Context

A unit plan document often includes a background or overview/rationale about the unit of work and why it is important that students learn this information. This is important in primary school science because learning must be situated in a real-world context of relevance to primary-aged students' lives beyond the science classroom. This captures students' interest in learning science and motivates them throughout the unit of work. For example, learning about forces may relate to sport. A unit of work situated in a real-world context relevant to students' lives might be centred around inquiry questions such as *How high does a ball bounce?* and *What material should be used to re-surface the multi-use sports courts at school?*

Assessment

Summative assessment is usually completed by the end of a unit of work and provides students an opportunity to demonstrate their knowledge, understanding and skills. A unit plan provides information about the type and conditions of summative assessment; when it occurs, including the duration and a description of what students are required to do. There should be a variety and balance of summative assessment types and conditions from unit to unit over one school year. Common summative assessment types in primary school science include investigations, model building, portfolios (journals) of learning, reports, response to stimulus (pictures/data) and tests. Common summative assessment conditions may include written, spoken and demonstration/performance. The local school/classroom context and the age and capabilities of students should be considered in the design of summative assessment. Chapter 7 explains further the assessment types and purposes in primary school science. What is important is that the summative assessment task provides an opportunity for students to demonstrate their achievement of the learning outcomes from the Australian Curriculum: Science. The curriculum's Achievement Standards are rewritten as statements of performance in a marking rubric and used to make consistent, comparable and defensible judgements about how well students have demonstrated what they know and what they can do.

Sequence of learning

Sequencing science learning is one of the major purposes of planning a unit of work. When planning a sequence of teaching and learning experiences, there are different pedagogical approaches that can be used. These include play- and discovery-based learning, inquiry-based learning, problem- or project-based learning and explicit teaching. There are many models to help teachers sequence lessons and activities so that the learning makes sense for students and smaller ideas develop over time into bigger ideas. The models presented in Snapshot 5.3 are examples of inquiry-based learning and promote a learner-centred approach consistent with constructivist learning theories.

Teaching strategies

The next step in planning a unit of work is identifying the specific teaching strategies. It is important to match the target science concept to an appropriate teaching strategy. Some common teaching strategies in primary school science that are explained in Chapter 6 include questioning, discussion, cooperative group work, play, investigation and inquiry. It is necessary to have a diverse range of teaching strategies, including both individual and group work, across a unit. The level of description of the teaching strategies is enough to provide an overview or *big picture* of what the teacher and students are doing each lesson. Snapshot 5.4 illustrates the meso level of description.

Micro level: lesson planning

Science lesson plans present your specific teaching and learning ideas and provide details about the specific actions of the teacher and students throughout the lesson (that is, what the teacher and students are actually doing). Your lesson is much more likely to be successful if your lesson plan clearly articulates what students will learn, how you will know that learning has taken place and how you intend students to learn it. There are a range of approaches to achieve this clarity. Many templates are available online for preservice and early career teachers that can be modified to suit the teacher's preferences or school and classroom context. A lesson plan generally includes the same information as a unit plan, but in a greater detail and specific to one lesson. In general, a specific science lesson should have an introduction, body and conclusion.

SNAPSHOT 5.3: Examples of inquiry learning models used to sequence learning in primary school science (Adapted from King, 2012)

Interactive model (Biddulph & Osborne, 1984)	5E Instructional approach (Bybee et al., 2006)	Orienting, enhancing, synthesising (Queensland School Curriculum Council [QSCC], 1999)	General inquiry model (Murdoch, 1998)
Preparation Teacher selects and researches topic.			
Exploration Students involved in topic through an exploratory activity. Students' prior knowledge is established.	Engage Students are engaged with an activity or question that affords opportunities for pre-existing ideas about the topic to be revealed.	Orientate Teacher introduces students to topic and elicits students' prior knowledge.	Tuning In Teacher provokes curiosity and wonder in new topic and elicits students' prior knowledge. Students formulate inquiry questions.
Student's questions Students are invited to ask questions about the topic.	Explore Students participate in activities where they can explore the concept. This may require the design of an inquiry question.	Enhance Activities are designed and implemented that afford students opportunities to construct knowledge of key concepts.	Finding Out/Sorting Out Students participate in learning activities where they are finding information. Students process and sort information.
Investigation Teacher and students select questions to explore. Students construct knowledge through investigations.	Explain Teacher provides opportunities for students to construct knowledge of key concepts to explain the phenomenon explored.		Going Further Students use new questions as the basis for new extended inquiry. Students share learnings with others.

(Continued)

SNAPSHOT 5.3: *Examples of inquiry learning models used to sequence learning in primary school science (Adapted from King, 2012) (Continued)*

Interactive model (Biddulph & Osborne, 1984)	5E Instructional approach (Bybee et al., 2006)	Orienting, enhancing, synthesising (Queensland School Curriculum Council (QSCC), 1999)	General inquiry model (Murdoch, 1998)
	Elaborate Students apply what they have learned to new situations.	Synthesise A blending of the canonical science with the real world. New terms and concepts are consolidated and reinforced.	Taking Action Students review and reflect on their own learning and new understanding and skills
Reflection Establishment of what has been ver-ified and what needs to be revisited.	Evaluate Students review and reflect on their own learning and new understanding and skills.		Reflection Teachers review the unit and reflect on students learning

Some schools sequence their lessons by closely following a program developed by the Australian Academy of Science (2020), *Primary Connections*, that is entirely based on the 5E Instructional Approach. Other schools modify these types of programs to suit their pedagogical approaches and interest and needs of their students.

SNAPSHOT 5.4: *An example of a unit plan—the first five lessons only*

Year 6 science	Electrical energy and circuits			
Rationale/Overview	Science Understanding	Science Inquiry Skills	Science as a Human Endeavour	General and Cross Curriculum Capabilities
Electrical energy is a part of children's daily lives and relates to energy production and use.	Physics: Electrical energy can be transferred and transformed in electrical circuits and can be generated from a range of sources	Communicating: Communicate ideas, explanations and processes using scientific representations in a variety of ways, including multimodal texts	Use and influence of science: Scientific knowledge is used to solve problems and inform personal and community decisions	Sustainability: Renewable energy
In this unit of work students will learn about electrical energy and circuits, applying what they have learned to make a simple circuit board to power an electrical device.				
	Learning and teaching activities		Diagnostic and formative assessment	Resources and safety
Engage Lesson 1 30 minutes	• Teacher introduces the problem of power outage—Lights Out!—for investigation		Students brainstorming *electricity* in KWL	Word wall for new vocabulary
	• Students complete a thought experiment to imagine what their life would be like without electricity			
	• Students start a KWL chart			

(Continued)

SNAPSHOT 5.4: An example of a unit plan—the first five lessons only (Continued)

Year 6 science		Electrical energy and circuits	Links to curriculum		
Explore	Lesson 2	30 minutes	• Students explore the classroom/schoolyard for objects that use electrical energy • Students draw energy transformation diagrams for three objects that use electrical energy	Teacher questions: What is electrical energy? Where does electrical energy come from?	Classroom/schoolyard walk in pairs with hat Worksheet
Explore	Lesson 3	60 minutes	• Students use trial-and-error to explore the components of an electrical circuit using an electricity kit • Students draw a labelled diagram of their circuit	Work sample—diagram	Electrical kit Worksheet
Explain	Lesson 4	60 minutes	• Teacher explains electric circuits using 'energy tokens' in a role play activity • Teacher shows flow of electrons in a circuit using online simulation • Students brainstorm possible analogies for electric circuits and share their ideas in a think-pair-share discussion	Teacher questions: What are the strengths and weaknesses of the models? Work sample—analogies	*Energy tokens* Online simulation (PhET)
Explain	Lesson 5	90 minutes	• Students use craft materials to create a stop motion animation (series of still photographs) to show how an electric circuit works and share their animation with the class	Work sample—animation	Craft materials

Lessons plans also contain additional information such as management, resources and safety considerations. An example of a science lesson plan for Year 2 on the topic of building materials is presented in Snapshot 5.5. Each of these aspects of a science lesson plan will be described in more detail in the following sections.

Introduction, body and conclusion

The main purpose of the beginning of a lesson is to capture students' interest in learning and provide motivation for the lesson. This might be achieved by posing a scenario, problem/challenge or question, reading a storybook or watching a video or conducting a scientific demonstration. Once students are engaged, the beginning of a lesson may then revisit learning from the previous lesson/s, so it can be connected to the new topic and built upon. This can be achieved through brainstorming, asking questions or using tools like a KWL (Know–Want to Know–Learned) chart. Activities at the beginning of a lesson are normally brief around 5–10 minutes.

The body of a lesson may be broken up into specific teaching and learning activities. For students, this may be exploring the science concept with hands-on materials, using data from an investigation to explain the science concept or applying and extending what they have learned to a new situation or context. These activities may occur individually or in collaborative groups. For the teacher, this may include a script of dialogue (e.g., a scientific explanation), a list of questions to prompt students' thinking or check for understanding, a description of how they will move around the classroom and interact with students (e.g., whole-class, small groups or individuals) and how the teaching and learning activities may need to be adapted or modified for students with particular needs. A lesson plan also lists specific resources or hands-on materials that will be needed (e.g., printouts, recyclable or craft materials and digital devices), including how many and whether there are any safety considerations.

The end of a science lesson is arguably the most important. In this part of the lesson, the *sense-making* occurs, and students can think deeply about what they have learned and link their learning to a big idea of science. The consolidation of science concepts may occur through discussion and explanation. At the end of a lesson, the teacher and students

SNAPSHOT 5.5: An example of a science lesson plan

Lesson title: Building materials	Subject: Science	Year level: 2	Duration: 45 minutes
Learning intentions: Students will be able to identify different materials and explain their properties	**Resources for students:** • Three objects of different weight, such as a tissue (straw), a plastic Duplo block (stick) and a container of playdough (brick) • Hairdryer and students' breath (wind)		**Resources for teachers:** • *Three Little Pigs* storybook • Predict–Observe sheets
Phase/Time allocation	**Teacher direction/activity/instruction:**		**Classroom management**
Introduction 10 minutes	• Read the *Three Little Pigs* • Ask questions about the materials used to build each house; What did the pigs use to build their houses? Why do you think the first two houses blew away? Which house was most stable? Why? • Ask students to list the properties of each material (straw, sticks, bricks) and suggest why they were suitable for building or not. What are the properties of the materials that did not work? What about the materials that did? • List in a table on the whiteboard three materials. Consider hard/soft, heavy/light, flexible/brittle.		• Sit on floor and listen to story • Reflect on story, answer questions

Body: Student inquiry and investigation 25 minutes	• Introduce experiment by posing questions: What other materials might be good for building? How can we find out? • Hand out three different objects and split class into five groups. Ask students to move to their groups. • Explain experiment. Ask students to decide on what form of *wind* they will use (hairdryer or their own breath). Model how to use the hairdryer • Outline group expectations: cooperative work, everyone has a go, discuss results, record on Predict–Observe sheets. Ask students to predict which items would be blown away by the wolf's huffing and puffing. Allow students to hold the items and make comparison. Record predictions on the worksheet. • Discuss comparative vocabulary, such as light, lighter, lightest or heavy, heavier, heaviest. • If finished early then ask students to work out how far it moved. • During experiment, circulate through class monitoring behaviour and eliciting students' understandings by asking questions: What have you noticed about the materials in each category? Why do you think you need to make sure the hairdryer is at the same place each time? • Can you tell me something about the materials that you think may be good or bad for building? Call class back to whole group scenario?	• Split into groups • Decide which *wind* they will use • Observe teacher's use of hairdryer • Do experiment in groups • Record results • Discuss reasons why the materials are suitable or not for building • Discuss results with whole class
Conclusion 10 minutes	• Revisit the book and review the materials the wolf was able to blow down and the one that was not. • Create a table of properties of good building materials on the whiteboard, use questions to elicit responses: What do you notice about all the materials that are good? What do they have in common? Would you say they are hard/soft, heavy/light? Do they move/bend? Did they pass the blow test? • Use questions to guide discussion about why some materials are suitable for building and others are not: Why do you think this material was/was not suitable? What do you think are the best materials for building/why? If you were going to build a house what would you use? Why?	• Make comparison to the materials that they have used and from the book • Provide reasons for choices regarding suitable and unsuitable materials
Formative assessment	• Work sample: Predict–Observe sheets	

may reflect upon the learning outcomes and evaluate whether they have been met through assessment techniques like questions, quizzes and the collection of work samples. At the end of a science lesson, conceptual connections with the next lesson can be made or students can be motivated for the next stage of their learning through intriguing problems or questions. Snapshot 5.5 is an example of a lesson plan for a Year 2 class.

Health and safety considerations

The health, safety and wellbeing of students involved in science curriculum activities must always be a priority. School leadership and teachers have a legal obligation and duty of care to ensure the safety of students when conducting science activities in schools and classrooms. As every science lesson is different, health and safety requirements will be different too. Many primary school science lessons have only minor safety considerations such as handling scissors and hot water, household items and household chemicals or working outside in the sun. Others, however, may involve more serious safety considerations like the use of hot plates or incorporation of flying projectiles. Some hazards in primary school science may include slippage, sunburn and allergic reactions. For all science lessons, a safety evaluation needs to be carried out to identify the severity and likelihood of safety issues and potential hazards. For school science investigations, many primary schools are using a web-based risk assessment tool, the *Primary RiskAssess* (Ecosolve Australia, 2020), as it provides information to teachers on this topic.

Summary of key points

Planning in science is important to ensure students' understanding develops towards the *big ideas of science* (Harlen, 2015) across the formal years of schooling and that there is alignment between curriculum, teaching and learning activities and assessment practices. Teachers most commonly engage in unit and lesson planning. In science, teachers use social constructivism as a referent so that students can build upon what they already know through collaborative, hands-on and engaging lesson activities. Lesson plans describe teaching and learning activities in detail and are documents that contain information about the topic, timing, teacher and student actions and physical resources.

Discussion questions

5.1. What is the purpose of planning at each level: whole-school, year-level, unit-level and lesson-level (refer to Figure 5.1)?

5.2. How will the Theory of Constructivism that you learned about in Chapter 2 help you to plan your primary school science lessons? What types of activities would you use in your lesson plans to support learning from a constructivist point of view? How would this differ for a lesson based on (a) personal, (b) social and (c) sociocultural constructivism?

5.3. How can a model, like those presented in Snapshot 5.4, help you when planning learning in primary school science? Select one of these frameworks and use it to plan a lesson or unit on a topic of your choosing.

5.4. How will you go about evaluating your planning documents when you have finished teaching your first unit of science? What information will you use in the evaluation?

5.5. How would you go about determining the safety risks of a primary science activity? What would you need to do from a safety point of view to allow Year 5 students to use hot glue guns in a science lesson?

5.6. Work your way through the lesson plan on building materials for Year 2 students presented in Snapshot 5.5 with a partner. Do you think you could successfully teach this lesson? What else do you need to know? What are the strengths and weaknesses of this lesson plan? How would you improve it?

References

Australian Academy of Science. (2020). *Primary connections*. Accessed July 20 2020 at: https://primaryconnections.org.au/.

Australian Curriculum, Assessment and Reporting Authority (ACARA). (2020). *Australian Curriculum: Science*. Accessed July 20 2020 at: https://www.australiancurriculum.edu.au/f-10-curriculum/science/.

Biddulph, F., & Osborne, R. (Eds.) (1984). *Making sense of our world: An interactive teaching approach*. Hamilton: NZ: University of Waikato.

Bybee, R. W., Taylor, J. A., Gardner, A., Van Scatter, P., Carlson Powell, J., Westbrook, A., & Landes, N. (2006). *BSCS 5E instructional model: Origins and effectiveness. A report prepared for the Office of Science Education, National Institutes of Health.* Colorado Springs, CO: Biological Science Curriculum Services.

Ecosolve Australia. (2020). *Primary RiskAssess*. Accessed July 20 2020 at: https://www.riskassess.com.au/info/primary_about.

Harlen, W. (2015). *Working with big ideas of science education.* Trieste, Italy: IAP.

King, D. (2012). Planning in secondary science. In G. Venville & V. Dawson (Eds.), *The art of teaching science for middle and secondary school* (pp. 84–103). Sydney, NSW: Allen & Unwin.

Murdoch, K. (1998). *Classroom connections: Strategies for integrated learning.* Melbourne: Eleanor Curtain Publishing.

Queensland Department of Education. (2020). *Providing the Australian Curriculum in Prep to Year 10 in Queensland state schools from 2017.* Accessed July 20 2020 at: https://education.qld.gov.au/curriculums/Documents/providing-curriculum.pdf.

Queensland School Curriculum Council (QSCC). (1999). *Years 1-10 Science Sourcebook Guidelines (Part 5 of 8).* Accessed July 2 2020 at: https://www.qcaa.qld.edu.au/downloads/p_10/kla_sci_sbg_05.pdf.

6

TEACHING STRATEGIES FOR PRIMARY SCHOOL SCIENCE

Pauline Roberts

Goals

The goals for this chapter are to support you to:

- Develop an understanding of effective approaches to teaching science
- Adopt inquiry-based approaches to teaching science

Australian Professional Standards for Teachers—Graduate Level:

- Standard 1: Know students and how they learn (Focus areas 1.2, 1.4, 1.5)
- Standard 2: Know the content and how to teach it (Focus areas 2.1, 2.2)
- Standard 3: Plan for and implement effective teaching and learning (Focus areas 3.1, 3.2, 3.3, 3.4, 3.5)
- Standard 4: Create and maintain supportive and safe learning environments (Focus areas 4.1, 4.2, 4.4)

Introduction

Effective science teaching is a critical goal for you as a primary school teacher. However, it is important for you to understand that there isn't one approach that will always work. Importantly, there is a vast spectrum of different teaching strategies that may be beneficial for your students if used appropriately. Making decisions about the overall approach you want to apply to teaching science in your classroom, what specific strategies to include and what you consider important in the process of students learning science may sound like a daunting matter, but this chapter is here to guide you through your considerations. In this chapter, I will start with various reasons for teaching science that you might adopt and the approaches that may align with these different viewpoints. I also make recommendations about using an inquiry-based approach to teach science. In discussing inquiry-based approaches, the specific teaching strategies that could be implemented are outlined, including some of the considerations to be aware of when applying these strategies. The information presented will allow you to focus on improving your science teaching wherever you are in your teaching career.

The focus of school science

Governments of developed countries emphasise science, and the work of scientists, as important for ongoing prosperity and growth within a competitive global economy. In most of these countries, like Australia, there is a focus on the results of international and national school student testing programs such as the Programme for International Student Assessment (PISA), Trends in International Mathematics and Science Study (TIMSS) and National Assessment Program—Literacy and Numeracy (NAPLAN). The results from these tests often produce an outcry in the mass media when these standards drop against competitors despite additional funding. A criticism of these assessment regimes is that they can result in a narrowing the curriculum to focus on specific content that might improve test scores rather than focussing on the process of learning.

An alternative to focusing on the outcomes of testing regimes may be that science and scientific literacy are the core of what we do as humans when trying to make sense of the world around us and understand our place within it. A scientific literacy perspective is more aligned with teaching approaches that engage students in science explorations and inquiries that are focused on the students' interests and questions and provide more authentic learning opportunities. When students are engaged in inquiry, they are better able to learn content knowledge, develop inquiry skills and an understanding of why we do science—to answer life's questions.

Scientific literacy as the focus of school science

Scientific literacy is concerned with the nature of science (see Chapter 1), as well as the reasons we consider science to be important. The Organisation for Economic Co-operation and Development (OECD) defines scientific literacy as 'the ability to engage with science-related issues, and with the ideas of science, as a reflective citizen' (OECD, 2017, p. 1). In Chapter 4, it was noted that the Australian Curriculum: Science highlights in its rationale that scientifically literate students have 'the ability to think and act in scientific ways [and that it] helps build the broader suite of capabilities in students as confident, self-motivated and active members of our society' (Australian Curriculum, Assessment and Reporting Authority [ACARA], 2016). These definitions of scientific literacy do not focus specifically on content knowledge, but instead highlight the processes of science and the capabilities and confidence people need to use science to solve problems in daily life and society. These viewpoints are further supported by the *Alice Springs (Mparntwe) Education Declaration* that focuses on education to develop confident and creative individuals who become active and informed citizens (Education Council, 2019). Moreover, these viewpoints are consistent with constructivism as a theory of knowledge (see Chapter 2) and inquiry as a pedagogical approach.

Inquiry-based approaches

Inquiry has been identified as an effective approach for teaching science knowledge, skills and dispositions. Duncan (2018) identified essential elements of inquiry including authenticity and relevance of the science topics being learned and a responsiveness of the curriculum to the students' interests. The essential elements of inquiry can be implemented through a range of teaching models and utilise various teaching strategies. Teachers need to understand the inquiry process in order to be able to provide opportunities and resources for students to develop scientific literacy. Two specific approaches to inquiry are outlined in the latter sections, the 5E Model and the 3-Stage Approach. Within the following sections, I also outline the specific teaching strategies that can be used.

The 5E Model

This model was developed by a team led by Roger Bybee as part of the Biological Sciences Curriculum Study in 1987. This model was adopted by the Australian Academy of Science (AAS) to provide the basis of the very successful *Primary Connections* (Australian Academy of Science [AAS], 2020) curriculum package for teaching science in Australian primary schools. The 5E Model is designed to provide students opportunities to learn through active, constructivist principles. The students are encouraged to:

> draw on their prior knowledge, pose questions, participate in hands-on experiences, and conduct exploratory and formal investigations, to develop their own explanations about scientific phenomena. Students are given opportunities to represent and re-represent their developing understanding using literacy skills. They are actively engaged in the learning process.
> (Australian Academy of Science [AAS], 2020, para 1)

As the name suggests, there are five stages to this teaching and learning model that students work through under the guidance of their teacher. Each of these phases serve a specific purpose in challenging existing knowledge and allowing opportunities to test and re-evaluate understandings towards the scientifically correct conclusions. The model provides a structure for an inquiry that can be implemented across several weeks, with resources available for all year levels and each content area in the Australian science curriculum. For more details of these resources and the professional learning opportunities on offer, go to www. primaryconnections.org.au. Snapshot 6.1 provides an outline of the 5E Model from the *Primary Connections* module *Under Our Feet* designed for Year 4 students to explore and develop understandings of soils, rocks and landscapes, and how they change over time.

The 3-Stage Approach

There are a number of inquiry models within the educational literature. What is common to a number of these approaches is the structured nature of the inquiry, frequently three steps, stages or phases as outlined later.

Stage 1 is an orientation phase where students are introduced to the topic. There is a brainstorm of ideas or questions, and initial planning is conducted to identify how to complete the inquiry. Sometimes called the

SNAPSHOT 6.1: Summary of Year 4 under our feet
Primary Connections module

Engage

Lesson 1: *Lost location* is designed to capture interest and find out what students know about soils, rocks and landscapes and how they change using a mystery treasure map and provocation and questioning through a brainstorm.

Explore

Lesson 2: *Studying soils* allows hands-on, group activities and discussion opportunities for students to test their current understanding of what is in soil.

Lesson 3: *Rock hard?*; Lesson 4: *Rollin' rock*; and Lesson 5: *Modelling mountains*, where students complete further hands-on explorations to investigate rocks, their features and how these change over time.

Explain

Lesson 6: *Fabulous formations* introduces students to the current scientific views of landscapes and how they form across time. This more teacher directed, explicit instruction style of lesson using images, websites and shared reading of factual texts.

Elaborate

Lesson 7: *Examining erosion* provides students the opportunity to plan and conduct an investigation into water erosion to test out the newly acquired knowledge from the Explain phase.

Evaluate

Lesson 8: *Meticulous maps* allows the students to review and reflect on their learning to represent what they know about erosion and how soils, rock, and landscapes change over time. The teacher completes summative assessment.

exploration phase, the focus is on identifying what students are interested in, what they already know and what they want to know more about—the students should pose the questions. Mind-maps or KWL charts (Know, Want to know, Learned) may be useful but effective *questions* are essential to guide the initial thoughts about the project or projects especially if students want to go off into different foci for their *group* inquiry.

In Stage 2, the investigation is where the hands-on work is completed through experiments, explorations or gathering of data. Depending on the topic identified, the questions asked and the chosen methods for data collection, the groups are busy with *researching, testing, collecting data* and *analysing results* of the inquiry project. The students will utilise skills across this phase to develop the content knowledge of their chosen topic, and so the process may look very different for each group. The *documentation* of the learning also occurs, and more questions might be raised as the initial ones are answered. The timeframe for this phase might be a week, a term or a whole year depending on the interest levels of the group and the complexity of the inquiry. Once the interest begins to wane, the inquiry will move to the final phase or stage.

Stage 3 represents the bringing together of the learning and a more formalised presentation for assessment purposes. Presentation ideas include a report, Floorbooks© (Warden, 1995), or an audio-visual or poster display to the class, parents or wider school community. The conclusion of the project allows the students to outline what they have learnt, how this has impacted them and where they think future inquiries might go. Sharing the information or communicating the findings are critical elements of the inquiry. Teachers should assist and allow for a range of presentation formats and assessment methods to be implemented.

Teaching strategies

There are numerous teaching strategies that can be used by the teacher as part of inquiry-based approaches to teaching. These include questioning, the use of provocations, group work and reflective tasks, explicit instruction, whole group and small group discussion, modelling, scaffolding, discussions, child-directed questions, scaffolding and opportunities for multi-modal representations. We explore some of these strategies in the following sections.

Discussion

Discussion as an inquiry process is an effective teaching tool that is used as a specific strategy to facilitate critical thinking and the development of understanding. Effective discussion relies on the successful use of questions (discussed later in the chapter). It requires students to listen attentively, accept other people's opinions and engage in reasoning (Killen, 2016). Discussion highlights the importance of language in shaping understanding and the importance of students being able to represent their ideas clearly to others. Discussion can occur in small groups or whole classes.

Discussion, when used as a teaching strategy, requires careful planning to ensure there is an academic focus on the outcomes of the lesson. Group discussions often require rules to be developed, so participants remain on topic and are respectful of opinions presented. The role of the teacher within discussions can be challenging because it requires skill to balance facilitation without taking over. The goal is for the students, not the teacher, to be talking! Finding this balance requires knowledge of the students, knowledge of the content and the skills to guide and prompt while making all students feel comfortable to contribute within the group environment. An effective discussion takes time to develop and should not be rushed. Reflection at the end of the discussion is critical as it enables the teacher to bring all perspectives together and consolidate learnings. Snapshot 6.2 outlines a great way to keep discussions on track with primary school students using a Talking Tub©.

Scaffolding

The strategy of scaffolding is used widely in the early years of schooling for all learning areas. Scaffolding refers to the process of providing temporary support for students that is slowly reduced as they become more competent in completing tasks for themselves (MacNaughton & Williams, 2009). Scaffolding can be used in a range of activities and in a range of ways, so that the students learn and gain confidence in their abilities to complete tasks alone.

In an inquiry approach, scaffolding assists in developing the skills of an inquiry until students have experience in completing projects for themselves. Depending on levels of experience scaffolding may look different for individual students, small groups or for the whole class

SNAPSHOT 6.2: An example of how to implement effective discussion with a Talking Tub©

Claire Warden, a Scottish educator and author, recommends the use of a *Talking Tub©* with children to promote discussion and keep learners on track as they develop skills of discussion. For example, a collection of shells, sponges, corals, weeds and sand can be placed in a large box decorated with an image of the ocean or a beach (or be blank to add to the mystery). Pieces of paper in different colours, sizes and shapes, pencils and markers can also be included along with magnifying glasses, digital microscopes and iPads and torches to assist in observations, exploration and note taking. Children sitting in a circle can remove items, examine them, communicate observations and discuss them in the group. These provocations can be sorted based on any number of categories the children establish and questions can be posed about where the items come from, what their purpose is, how they may be related. Depending on interest, this activity could develop into an inquiry about an array of marine life, sustainability, weather and climate, erosion, protective clothing, adaptation, SCUBA diving, waves, beaches, seafood, food chains…. The possibilities are endless!

The skills needed to operate successfully in a discussion should be taught. How students present their point of view, listen to others and accept comments and ideas and collaborate in thinking within a group are required skills. A simple brainstorm chart where every-one's ideas are added can start developing this understanding and can build towards KWL charts or KWHL (Know, Wonder, How learned). Floorbooks© can also allow multiple student voices to be recorded and shared.

as competence evolves. Scaffolding can occur in relation to the level of inquiry questions, data collection or results. Higher levels of scaffolding may involve these being provided for students while reduced scaffold-ing may give students more control over these tasks. Some students who struggle with groupwork or with individual learning, may require the scaffolding to remain in place longer, until they are operating in the inquiry process independently. An example of scaffolding are tables—such as those used in *Primary Connections*, that are created to prompt students through an inquiry, so they know what elements they need to consider in their planning. As the students become more proficient in doing inquiries, the detail in these tables can be reduced and eventually eliminated as the students know what they need to include.

Explicit instruction

The role of explicit instruction within a science inquiry is to provide students with teacher-led input regarding the correct scientific understanding of concepts. Explicit instruction is a teacher-centred approach that usually takes place as part of a whole group session where content is delivered by the teacher in a formal way (Killen, 2016). Within a broader inquiry approach to instruction, the purpose of explicit instruction is to focus on academic content, to monitor and test students' understanding of the content and provide clear and direct feedback to ensure directly observable learning (Killen, 2016). Within the 5E Model, this teaching strategy is usually implemented within the *Explain* phase which occurs after students' prior knowledge has been identified.

Explicit instruction can be an efficient way to introduce new content. It reduces cognitive overload on students by not requiring them to use their working memory because the information is provided for them (Kirschner, Sweller & Clark, 2006). An explicit instruction lesson also needs less hands-on resources and can concentrate teacher and students on the learning outcomes rather than the process of learning and can, therefore, take less time (Killen, 2016).

Concerns have been raised about using explicit instruction and these should be considered in applying this strategy. One main concern is a reduced opportunity for differentiation for individual students within lessons because prior knowledge is unlikely to be the same for all. Ineffective teacher-led lessons may also be less engaging for students, resulting in them losing focus and missing vital content. Another consideration is the possibility of students relying on the teacher as the source of information rather than developing their own skills to develop understanding, participate in discussions or plan their own learning sequence. There are fewer opportunities for the teacher to identify students' prior knowledge or any alternative conceptions (see Chapter 3);

fewer opportunities for students to develop thinking skills such as analysing, problem-solving and decision-making; and fewer opportunities for students to reflect on their learning (Killen, 2016). The use of explicit instruction within the phases of the 5E Model, however, addresses some of these concerns through the use of other strategies in other stages of the 5E Model. Because of these limitations, explicit instruction is a useful teaching approach to be used as one in a sequence of different approaches, not a teaching process on its own.

Multimodal representation

Documentation of learning 'provides a written or pictorial account of what has occurred' (MacNaughton & Williams, 2009, p. 296) allowing students to reflect on their learning experience and revisit and consolidate their understanding of the content. Documentation modes include, photos of the students while they work as well as what they have created through the process; videos of groups working or of students reporting what they have done; audio recordings to accompany models that have been built, written notes from the teacher and the students as they problem-solve or any combination of these methods. Allowing students to use a range of modes in representing their understanding allows for diversified assessments and allows teachers to mirror the capabilities of a range of students.

Writing is an important strategy in science because engagement in writing encourages students to think and problem-solve as they record their thinking processes. Deeper understanding is required when students are asked to analyse and organise their ideas. These metacognitive processes can be further diversified by varying the type of writing task to be completed. For example, students can be asked to write a description of what they did or an exposition that explains their thinking processes. Alternatively, they can be asked to write a narrative account of an inquiry experience that persuades the reader of their point of view gained from the exploration. The type of writing will be determined by the purpose of the task, the skill level of the students and what you want students to achieve.

Embodied learning incorporates movement in the learning process and allows students to connect and demonstrate knowledge in different ways. Play-based approaches, for example, allow students to explore problems through play scenarios and centres and can encompass embodied learning as students are actively engaged in the observation or investigation process. Embodied learning may include throwing beanbags while counting or physically manipulating objects as part of solving a science problem or include role play where students dramatise roles associated with real-world situations.

Questions and questioning

One of the most critical elements of inquiry at all stages is the teacher's ability to use questions effectively. High-quality questions promote thinking and can invoke curiosity which young students seem to have in abundance but has been shown to decrease as students' progress through primary school (Duncan, 2018). Questions can be used to guide, scaffold, extend, clarify, unite, challenge and many other aspects of the inquiry process. There are a number of frameworks or categories of questions that you may be familiar with from other areas of your study. Bloom's taxonomy is one of the most well-known questioning frameworks which, when used, can support teachers to improve the quality of their questions by using specific verbs such as to *classify* objects or *discuss* their understanding.

An alternate framework that can be used for high-quality questioning is that developed by Christine Chin specifically for science teachers. In this research, Chin (2007) identified questioning approaches including *socratic questioning*, *verbal jigsaw*, *semantic tapestry* and *framing* to stimulate productive thinking in students and develop discursive skills in teachers.

Group work and cooperative learning

Very few tasks in the modern world are completed in isolation. Working as part of a team is important in all occupations, and in science, workplaces employ teams of researchers working together to solve problems. The skills required to engage in teamwork are fostered in schools when students complete group work and team projects in many discipline areas, including science.

According to Killen (2016), group work can shift the focus for students to more active learning and encourage less reliance on the teacher. Group work can also improve communication skills through requiring additional verbalisation of ideas in a non-threatening environment. Students can take on leadership roles and solve complex problems related to real-world tasks that can be differentiated to meet the needs of the students within the groups. These outcomes, however, require careful group selection and the development of cooperative learning skills.

Working collaboratively can take place in a range of group sizes that can be designed based on a number of different criteria. You might arrange small groups based on students' interests, abilities levels, friendship groups or location depending on the task and the level or type of peer learning you are trying to encourage. You may like to assign roles to members within the group and these may be rotated on different projects or within the same project. Teachers should be aware that the composition of the group may impact on the levels of participation within the group as well as the success of the peer learning strategies being used.

Group work will require the teaching of collaborative learning strategies as students may not have experienced them prior to joining your class. Collaborative learning requires tasks that can be completed in groups and also an incentive structure that allows each member to feel achievement and that they have role to play (Killen, 2016).

An example of a cooperative task is when a group designs an investigation (scaffolded appropriately) and then each person takes on a role in completing different stages of the investigation. The *Primary Connections* resources include specific roles for children within groups such as the *Manager* who is responsible for material collection and return; the *Speaker* who has the job of asking questions of other teams or the teacher, and the *Director* who keeps the team on track and monitors the steps of the investigation. These roles can be modified to suit the task at hand and the levels of the students in completing collaborative work.

Summary of key points

In this chapter, we have examined the underlying beliefs that impact on the teaching of science in the primary school classroom. The text describes two specific models for an inquiry approach to teaching science—The 5E Model and the 3-Stage Approach. Furthermore, specific teaching strategies used within these models are described. The strategies emphasise active approaches to learning and the use of effective questions and discussion to engage students in learning about real-life contexts and problems.

Discussion questions

6.1. Why is it important to consider your views about teaching science and students' learning?

6.2. How does your role as the teacher differ when the focus is on an inquiry-based approach to teaching compared with explicit instruction? Is it possible to use explicit instruction as part of an inquiry-based approach? Are inquiry and explicit instruction mutually exclusive teaching approaches or are they complementary?

6.3. Work with a partner or small team to develop a series of up to five lessons using the 3-Stage Approach of inquiry for a class of Year 3 students about the effect of heat on solid and liquids.

6.4. Explore the *Primary Connections* (Australian Academy of Science [AAS], 2020) curriculum resources for Year 4 Chemical Sciences, All Mixed Up. What questions do you think that Year 4 students might have about mixtures and their uses during the Explore phase? How will you encourage and motivate them to ask interesting and helpful questions? When it comes to the Explain phase of this module of work on mixtures, what are you confident to explain and what are you currently not confident to explain? What will you do to improve your confidence?

References

Australian Academy of Science (AAS). (2020). *Primary connections*. Accessed October 30 2020 at: https://www.primaryconnections.org.au.

Australian Curriculum, Assessment and Reporting Authority (ACARA). (2016). *Australian Curriculum*. Accessed October 30 2020 at: https://www.acara.edu.au/.

Australian Institute for Teaching and School Leadership (AITSL). (2017). *Australian professional standards for teachers*. Accessed October 30 2020 at: https://www.aitsl.edu.au/.

Chin, C. (2007). Teacher questioning in science classrooms: Approaches that stimulate productive thinking. *Journal of Research in Science Teaching, 44*(6), 815–843.

Duncan, R. (Ed.). (2018). *Journeys of inquiry*. Perth: Australian Independent Schools Western Australia (AISWA).

Education Council. (2019). *Alice Springs (Mparntwe) Education Declaration*. Education Services Australia. Accessed August 7 2020 at: https://docs.education.gov.au/system/files/doc/other/final_-_alice_springs_declaration_-_17_february_2020_security_removed.pdf.

Killen, R. (2016). *Effective teaching strategies: Lessons from research and practice* (7th ed.). South Melbourne: Cengage Learning Australia.

Kirschner, P. A., Sweller, J., & Clark, R. E. (2006). Why minimal guidance during instruction does not work: An analysis of the failure of constructivist, discovery, problem-based, experiential, and inquiry-based teaching. *Educational Psychologist, 41*(2), 75–86.

MacNaughton, G., & Williams, G. (2009). *Teaching techniques for teaching young children: Choices for theory and practice* (3rd ed.). Melbourne: Pearson.

Organisation for Economic Co-operation and Development (OECD). (2017). *PISA for development brief—2017/2.* Accessed August 7 2020 at: https://www.oecd.org/pisa/pisa-for-development/10-How-PISA-D-measures-science-literacy.pdf.

Warden, C. (1995). *Talking and thinking Floorbooks: An approach to consultation, observation, planning and assessment in children's learning.* Scotland: Mindstretchers.

7

ASSESSMENT, LEARNING AND TEACHING

Debra Panizzon

Goals

The goals for this chapter are to support you to:

- Understand how assessment, learning and teaching are intrinsically linked
- Outline the key components underpinning quality assessment processes
- Recognise how increasing accountability can influence teacher practices around assessment

Australian Professional Standards for Teachers—Graduate level:

- Standard 1: Know students and how they learn (Focus areas 1.3, 1.5)
- Standard 2: Know the content and how to teach it (Focus areas 2.3)
- Standard 5: Assess, provide feedback and report on student learning (Focus areas 5.1, 5.2, 5.3)

Introduction

Isn't assessment really about identifying what students have learnt? I have never really given it much thought. I assume when I am finishing up a section or unit of work and need some idea about what my students know, I'll assess them. They might write something or fill in a worksheet so I know what they have leant! (Sarah, beginning primary school preservice teacher).

Having read Sarah's quote, how closely do your views of assessment align with hers? How do your views differ? While Sarah expressed a number of ideas about assessment, most are either very traditional or limited in their view. The purpose of this chapter is to explore the nature and purpose of assessment in relation to primary school science in the hope of validating some of your own ideas while broadening and challenging others.

In general, assessment is about gathering and interpreting information about students' learning (Resnick & Schantz, 2017). In science, *student learning* includes scientific understandings, processes, skills, attitudes and values, which is quite different to other discipline areas. Ultimately, assessment in science is about finding out *what students know, understand* and *can actually do* across all of these areas (Panizzon & Pegg, 2008).

The link between student learning and assessment is often straight-forward but less so is the critical role of assessment in guiding teacher planning and practice. Cross (1998, p. 6) explained this as:

Classroom assessment informs teachers how effectively they are teaching and students how effectively they are learning. Through classroom assessment, teachers get continual feedback on whether and how well students are learning what teachers hope they are teaching. And students are required, through a variety of class-room assessment exercises, to monitor their learning, to reflect on it, and to take corrective action while there is still time left.

Thinking of assessment in this manner moves it from being merely a task that occurs at the end of a teaching sequence (as viewed by Sarah) to an ongoing process that continually monitors student learning and progress in science. Teachers do this using a range of non-verbal, verbal and written cues from their students. What is critical in doing this is that teachers identify where students might need additional support or help. They use the information gained to modify their teaching to address their students' needs. This intrinsic connection between assessment, learning and teaching is represented in Figure 7.1. Having identified the learning

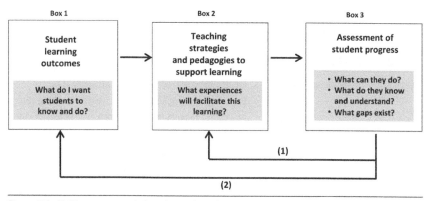

Figure 7.1 Linking assessment, learning and teaching.

outcomes to be addressed (Box 1), teachers plan strategies using pedagogies to support student learning (Box 2) while continually gauging student progress (Box 3). In turn, this provides feedback for teachers who then modify the experiences they offer students (see 1), while monitoring student progress against the intended learning outcomes continues (see 2). Hence, assessment is useful for the both the student and the teacher.

Understanding the nature of this relationship and how it can be achieved in teaching primary science to ensure equity for students are the foci for this chapter. Initially, the different types of assessment and their purposes in education are described. Following this, tasks and activities suitable for assessing students' learning in primary science are explored. Finally, ways of ensuring quality and equitable practices are then discussed in relation to current pressures that are impacting teachers as they juggle classroom assessment in a world of increasing high-stakes accountability. This chapter deliberately sets out to inform and challenge your views of assessment and its role in student learning and your own teaching.

Using assessment for different purposes

Assessment is often categorised as diagnostic, formative, summative or evaluative depending upon its intended purpose. In the late 1990s, alternative categories known as *assessment for learning*, *assessment of learning* and *assessment as learning* emerged from the work of Black and Wiliam (1998). The alignment between these two different categories and their purposes are summarised in Table 7.1.

Table 7.1 Assessment types and purposes

Types		Purposes
Traditional	*Black and Wiliam (1998)*	
Diagnostic	*Assessment for learning*	Identify the initial conceptions of students at the beginning of a teaching sequence so that teaching can be planned to build upon the current conceptions of students, e.g., use of concept cartoons and concept maps.
Formative	*Assessment for learning*	Provide informal and continual feedback to students about their learning in science. This promotes positive encouragement and guidance to students about how they might improve their work. As teachers we use this information to guide our teaching while supporting and enhancing student learning.
Summative	*Assessment of learning*	Collect evidence using varying tasks to assess students formally against curriculum achievement standards, which are then reported to the parents/guardians and students. Usually the most commonly known type of assessment.
	Assessment as learning	Encourage students to reflect on their own learning. What are their strengths and weaknesses? How do they learn best? This thinking is extremely powerful because it helps students become metacognitive about themselves as learners.
Evaluative		Not immediately relevant to classroom teachers because it is about the measurement and assessment of student learning more generally. It involves monitoring cohorts of students over time and analysing the patterns in the data. This type of assessment is used for teacher and educational accountability purposes by governments.

While similarities between the sets of categories are evident, there are three key points of difference in those devised by Black and Wiliam (1998):

1. Emphasise assessment as being integrated with student learning and teaching. For Black and Wiliam, assessment informs teachers about what students can do while highlighting gaps in their learning. This provides guidance to the teacher about where to direct their teaching.

2. Recognise that *assessment for learning* is pivotal in supporting student learning because ongoing feedback helps students know where to focus their attention and enhance their own learning.

3. Acknowledge *assessment as learning* whereby students too have responsibility for their own learning. Encouraging students to think about how they learn helps them become metacognitive and self-regulated in their learning, which is extremely powerful. *Metacognition* is a process when students think about and analyse their own thinking and learning.

The terms by Black and Wiliam (1998) are applied in this chapter.

Diversification of assessment tasks is key

The activities, tasks and strategies selected to assess students' progress should depend on the purpose of assessment, the year level of your students and the intended learning outcomes. For example, a student talks to the class, for example, about their investigation on the phases of the Moon, could be used as *assessment for learning* with teachers and peers providing feedback to help the student develop their ideas further. However, the same task could be used as *assessment of learning* with the teacher marking and grading the work in some way and recording the result. Unfortunately, teachers can get locked into thinking that only certain tasks can be used for this type of assessment, which is not the case. We know from research that students' conversations, digital products, such as videos and photographs, and portfolios containing their most prized work are valuable sources of evidence that demonstrate what primary students know and can do in science (Fensham & Rennie, 2013). It is your responsibility as classroom teacher to use your professional judgement to decide the most appropriate tasks for assessing students in science.

Gauging students' initial ideas

The purpose of assessment activities used at the beginning of a teaching sequence is to determine students' existing understandings so that teaching can be designed to stimulate students in building and restructuring their existing scientific understanding. Determining students' existing understandings prior to teaching is based on the theory of constructivism (see Chapter 2) and is a key indicator of quality teaching. It's also a great way to get to know your students.

- *Brainstorming:* This refers to the process of generating a range of ideas or solutions through open discussion with students. While often used to gauge the prior knowledge of students, it can also be used to get students thinking about an area or question in science. All ideas can be summarised on a board or captured electronically. For example, you might ask Year 5 students to brainstorm their ideas about *how shadows are made* before embarking on a series of investigations on shadows and light sources.

  Brainstorming can be extended by allowing students to write questions they have about an area of science, which are posted to a Question Wall. When a student thinks a question has been answered, they go to the wall, select the question and provide the answer for it. This strategy encourages students to be metacognitive (i.e., *assessment as learning*), responsible for their own learning and to recognise when they have learnt something new (i.e., *assessment for learning*). However, it is possible to allocate marks to students as a question on the Question Wall is answered, and they explain the answer to others (i.e., *assessment of learning*).

- *Concept maps:* These visual displays encourage students to demonstrate links and connections between different concepts (see Figure 7.2). Students can develop maps at the beginning of a teaching sequence

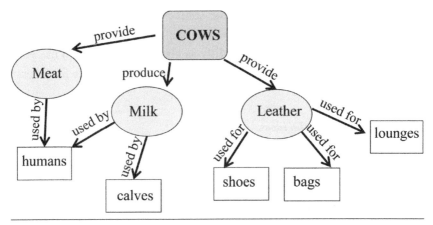

Figure 7.2 Example of a concept map—cows.

and then review them at the end using two different colours. With teacher guidance, students can compare and contrast between the two versions identifying the changes in their scientific understandings. As an example, the map below might be expected at the end of a teaching sequence having learnt about cows as living things and their uses to humans.

Observations and individual conferences with students

Teachers make observations constantly in their classrooms. By focusing on specific students, it is possible to gain a clear sense of their progress from their engagement with a specific task, the skills they demonstrate, such as measuring and collecting data, and their level of understanding of scientific concepts. Time spent asking students questions and carefully listening to their answers immediately highlights areas of difficulty, hence an opportunity for you to provide constructive feedback to facilitate learning. For example, listening to Year 5 students' ideas about how big they think the Earth is compared to the Moon, the Sun and other planets in the Solar System may give insights about how to develop a modelling activity to dispel alternative conceptions students hold, such as 'The Moon is bigger than Venus, Saturn and Jupiter'.

Student voice—oral and written

Oral and written assessment tasks require students to provide a considered response using the knowledge and skills they have learned. Within primary school, these tasks can be quite diverse in nature.

- *Research a topic*: Teachers identify a particular area for exploration by their students for example, comparing the features of animals living in very different climates on Earth. In planning this task for students, you must be clear about the learning outcomes being targeted and ensure that students are clear about what they are being asked to do. For example, you might discuss with them some of the key ideas they might seek information about. Without this type of direction or scaffolding, many primary school students are left with little idea about what they need to do, with parents sometimes playing a major role in the final product produced by students.

- *Reflective entries or journals:* This type of activity encourages students to move beyond a diary entry of what is completed during a lesson to thinking over what they have actually learnt; that is, noticing how their ideas and understandings have changed and developed. With students less experienced with reflective entries, it is useful to stimulate their thinking using questions that build the skills necessary for reflection of their work. Examples might include, 'What did I learn today?' 'How does this differ to my earlier ideas?' 'What was easy for me?' 'What might I need more help with?'
- *Portfolio:* Represents a selection of a student's work over a period of time, which is used to demonstrate the growth and development of scientific understandings and skills. There is a degree of ownership for the student in choosing the work that best illustrates their learning. *Reflections about their learning* might form part of this portfolio. Collectively, portfolios and student reflections are very powerful metacognitive tools for the student with both appropriate for *assessment for* and *of* learning.
- *Presentations:* Role-plays, storyboards, posters, PowerPoints and iMovies are other ways to assess students. Once more, identify the learning outcomes to be assessed upfront because it is easy to become *taken in* by sophisticated electronic representations that really demonstrate little deep understanding of science.

Practical and investigative activities

These types of activities whether undertaken in the classroom or outdoors are crucial for students to develop scientific skills and an understanding of the processes of science. Practical activities should also support students in developing their understandings of scientific concepts.

- *Predict–Observe–Explain (POE):* These comprise three distinct phases. First, students are introduced to a situation where a change will result from an action and asked to *predict* what is likely to occur. Second, the change is demonstrated with students *observing* the outcomes. Finally, students propose an *explanation* for their observations while explaining any differences they notice between what they predicted and what occurred. Snapshot 7.1 provides a working example.

> **SNAPSHOT 7.1: *Movement of a car down a ramp***
>
> A small car is held at the top of a ramp. Students are asked to predict what they think will happen when the car is released. Predictions can be noted individually, in a group or collectively on the board. The car is released with all observations noted. This process is repeated a number of times. Students now have the task of explaining any differences between their predictions and observations. Further questions can then be posed, such as: *What would happen to the car if I raise the ramp further from the floor? What about if I lower it?*

POEs provide an engaging way of introducing a scientific concept to students while developing their scientific skills. Using strategic questioning, the teacher can use these kinds of activities to clearly identify those students who require further probing with their thinking and those who are ready to move forward.

- *Investigations and/or fair tests:* Practical work can involve students completing a specific procedure where they control particular factors (i.e., fair test) through to more open-ended investigations where students develop an inquiry question to explore. In terms of assessment, there are two aspects to consider, (i) the scientific skills, such as being able to make observations, measure accurately using appropriate devices, recording results; and (ii) the ability to draw conclusions and interpretations from the results. Teachers need to think carefully about how to assess both of these components appropriately. For example, assessing whether students can measure the distance a car has travelled must be observed by the teacher. If you assess this skill through a student's response to a worksheet, you may be assessing work copied from elsewhere.
- *Building models/dioramas:* The construction of 3D models encourages students to demonstrate their scientific understandings through physical representations. For example, a model of an energy efficient room in their home with the key features identified.

Tests, quizzes or worksheets

Essentially tests, quizzes and worksheets are similar forms of assessment with the only difference related to their purpose. Tests are completed individually by students and used most often as *assessment of learning*. These are likely to be used more frequently in the upper years of primary school. Quizzes tend to be done collectively or individually as *assessment for learning*. Worksheets might be used either way. However, regardless of purpose, it is imperative that the items or questions used encourage students to explain and apply their conceptual understandings of science; demonstrate their scientific skills and knowledge of the processes of science; and, the ways in which science helps them to interpret their world. The items *should not* just be about students memorising and regurgitating scientific facts. Limiting the types of items used in these forms of assessment may advantage some students over others raising inequity (American Association for the Advancement of Science [AAAS], 2007).

Strategic questioning

Questioning during teaching is one of the most powerful strategies for assessing the progress of students in an ongoing manner. Careful questioning allows a teacher to draw out students' understandings and alternative conceptions in science (Reinsvold & Cochran, 2012). Both the level of responses provided by students and the number of students prepared to respond to your questions gives immediate feedback about which students might be struggling with particular aspects of the lesson, i.e., *assessment for learning*. But equally important is that worksheets and tests used for the *assessment of learning* comprise questions that target particular learning outcomes. As teachers, we can hinder our students from demonstrating their actual level of achievement in science (Panizzon & Pegg, 2008) by not thinking carefully about the types of questions and tasks we are using with our students. The art of constructing and posing questions along with other teaching strategies that could be used for assessment are discussed in Chapter 6.

Assessment practices to ensure quality and equity

Assessment must be fair and equitable to all students. Any task or activity used to assess students should allow them to explain, demonstrate and communicate their learning in science. It should not set out to identify *what they do not know,* which is a perception held by some teachers. It is your responsibility to be clear about the expectations and the learning outcomes being targeted, especially with *assessment of learning*. It is also critical that these expectations are shared with your students so they are not confused. For example, discussing the criteria upfront that will be used to assess their work provides direction to students about where to focus their learning while reducing their anxiety. Some teachers have difficulty with this idea considering that if students know the criteria, they will all achieve highly. Actually, this is not the case because students respond to any task using their constructed knowledge, which cannot be prompted just by knowing the assessment criteria.

Rubrics

One common way to communicate assessment expectations to students is through *rubrics*. In brief, rubrics make explicit the outcomes to be achieved as steps involved in the learning process. A rubric is designed for a specific assessment task and helps to align the assessment criteria to the learning outcomes and the curriculum achievement standards. An example is provided in Snapshot 7.2. In this rubric, the curriculum achievement standard for the scientific understandings strand for living things in the Australian Curriculum (ACARA, 2020) is unpacked for Year 4 students.

While rubrics are helpful in ensuring consistency and equity in assessing students for a particular task, developing clear and consistent rubrics requires considerable practice. The *Primary Connections* website has a range of useful resources including assessment rubrics that are extremely useful.

Feedback

A key step when assessing our students is to provide feedback (Hattie & Timperley, 2007). This does not simply mean a comment, such as 'a good try'. While such comments are positive, they do not help the student understand how they might improve their understanding. Snapshot 7.3 provides an inspiring YouTube clip demonstrating the power of good quality feedback in helping young students improve their achievement.

While the clip in Snapshot 7.3 relates specifically to students' drawing skills, the principles regarding feedback are relevant to any task

SNAPSHOT 7.2: Living things assessment rubric for Year 4

Achievement standard (scientific understandings)	Level of achievement		
	Below achievement standard	At achievement standard	Above achievement standard
Describe relationships that assist the survival of living things and sequence key stages in the life cycle of a plant or animal.	• Provides simple observations of the stages in the life cycle of an insect, e.g., butterfly. • Notes a relationship between an insect and its food source. • Lists things that help the food source of the insect to grow.	• Sequences the key stages of the life cycle of an insect, e.g., butterfly • Describes and explains the relationship between an insect and its food source that helps it to live and grow. • Describes the things the food source needs to continue growing.	• Provides detailed information for each of the life cycle stages and the processes involved in the changes to the insect, e.g., butterfly. • Demonstrates a detailed understanding of the relationships existing between an insect, its food source and other animals that ensures the insect's survival.

SNAPSHOT 7.3: Quality feedback

View the YouTube clip, *Austin's butterfly: Building excellence in student work* at: https://www.youtube.com/watch?v=E_6PskE3zfQ

This clip shows clearly how the quality of students' work can be improved with students when feedback is constructive and specific in terms of what could be improved.

Reflection: What do you consider are the key messages raised about feedback in this clip?

in science. Hattie and Timperley (2007) identified four levels of teacher feedback:

- *Task level:* Focus on how well *the task* is completed with the teacher suggesting more, different or correct information, e.g., 'You need to have six legs'.
- *Process level:* Focus on *the process* needed to finish a task with feedback targeting the learning needed to complete the work, e.g., 'You need to change this part of your wing using the ideas we discussed earlier'.
- *Self-regulation level:* Focus on building skills around self-evaluation and confidence in order to engage further on the task, e.g., 'You can see in the photograph the key features of the butterfly. Compare your picture to identify changes that you need to make to align more closely with this photograph'. Note that this level is not especially relevant for this drawing task with these younger students because they actually need more directed feedback.
- *Personal level:* Focus on the *person* or *self* that is unrelated to the actual task, e.g., 'How cute!'

Which of these levels do you think are used most often by teachers? You probably guessed correctly, the Task and Personal levels. However, it is the Process and Self-regulation levels that maximise student achievement because they *empower students to become more effective learners.*

Developing professional judgement

There are no rules about what tasks should be used when *assessing of* or *for learning* in primary science. As such, no attempt has been made in this chapter to categorise the different ways of monitoring student progress. This is left to your professional judgement. As a teacher, you need to select assessment tasks that, (i) are appropriate to the science learning outcomes being targeted; and (ii) inform your students about their progress in fair and equitable ways.

Having stressed these points, it is important to be aware that assessment can be controversial because it is often used by governments and other stakeholders to raise educational and political accountability. Unfortunately, this creates considerable confusion and anxiety for classroom teachers (Klenowski & Wyatt-Smith, 2012). A clear example of this is the National Assessment Program – Literacy and Numeracy (NAPLAN) test with the data often used by the media and government authorities to undermine the community perception of the quality of states/territories, schools and individual teachers. The purpose of NAPLAN is evaluative (review Table 7.1 earlier in this chapter), yet the results are often used to make assumptions about the overall achievement of students in specific classrooms across Australia. This is interesting given that NAPLAN is not mandatory with parents and schools able to exclude their children from involvement in the test.

These accountability pressures can impact primary teachers in their classroom practices. One of the most immediate outcomes is *teaching-to-the-test* in countries like Australia, the United Kingdom and the United States (Klenowski & Wyatt-Smith, 2012). In Australia, so strong is this growing culture that teachers have been reprimanded, even dismissed, for coaching their students during NAPLAN tests. This demonstrates the increasing demands being placed on teachers to attain high results for their students on these large-scale, highly accountable tests where teachers should be supported to focus on the day-to-day progress of their students.

Summary of key points

Assessment is intrinsically linked to learning and teaching—it is not something that happens at the end of a teaching sequence. Assessment informs students about what they know and can do in science while allowing teachers to use the information to plan lessons that enhance student learning in a more targeted manner. Primary teachers need to be proficient in using a range of assessment tasks so that they can select those most appropriate for assessing students against the intended learning outcomes. Collecting evidence of student achievement in science requires quality items that are fair and equitable to provide all students with an opportunity to succeed in science.

Discussion questions

　　7.1. Explain why it is important to use a range of different tasks when assessing students in science. Who should choose which tasks to use and why should this be the case?

　　7.2. How does assessment impact your teaching? Refer to your own learning experiences in discussing this question.

7.3. Fair and equitable assessment is critical. Explain what this state-ment means in relation to teaching primary school science. How can this be achieved by primary school teachers? What role does teacher feedback play in terms of providing greater equity for primary school students?

References

Australian Curriculum, Assessment and Reporting Authority (ACARA). (2020). *Australian Curriculum: Science*. Accessed September 13 2020 at: www.australiancurriculum.edu.au/f-10-curriculum/science/.

American Association for the Advancement of Science (AAAS). (2007). Science literacy for a changing future. *2061 Today Newsletter, 17*(1), 1–8.

Black, P., & Wiliam, D. (1998). Assessment and classroom learning. *Assessment in Education, 5*(1), 7–74.

Cross, P. K. (1998). Classroom research: Implementing the scholarship of teaching. *New Directions for Teaching and Learning, 75,* 5–12.

Fensham, P. J., & Rennie, L. J. (2013). Towards authentically assessed science curriculum. In D. Corrigan, R. Gunstone, & A. Jones (Eds.), *Valuing assessment in science education: Pedagogy, curriculum, policy* (pp. 69–100). Dordrecht: Springer.

Hattie, J., & Timperley, H. (2007). The power of feedback. *Review of Educational Research, 77*(1), 81–112.

Klenowski, V., & Wyatt-Smith, C. (2012). The impact of high stakes testing: The Australian story. *Assessment in Education: Principles, Policy & Practice, 19*(1), 65–79.

Reinsvold, L. A., & Cochran, K. F. (2012). Power dynamics and questioning in elementary science classrooms. *Journal of Science Teacher Education, 23*(7), 745–768.

Panizzon, D., & Pegg, J. (2008). Assessment practices: Empowering mathematics and science teachers in rural secondary schools to enhance student learning. *International Journal of Science and Mathematics Education, 6,* 417–436.

Resnick, L. B., & Schantz, F. (2017). Testing, teaching, learning: Who is in charge? *Assessment in Education: Principles, Policy and Practice, 24*(3), 424–432.

8

DIGITAL PEDAGOGIES FOR PRIMARY SCHOOL SCIENCE

Wendy Nielsen and Matthew Kearney

Goals

The goals for this chapter are to support you to:

- Describe categories of educational technologies that can be used to support primary school students to learn science
- Distinguish between techno-centric and pedagogical reasons for selecting digital resources
- Appreciate the range of digital pedagogies and resources available to primary school teachers

Australian Professional Standards for Teachers—Graduate level:

- Standard 2: Know the content and how to teach it (Focus area 2.6)
- Standard 3: Plan for and implement effective teaching and learning (Focus area 3.4)

Introduction

New educational technologies have been regularly introduced and hailed as *game changers* in schools. In the early 20th century, film and radio were introduced as resources in schools and now include mobile devices and associated applications (or *apps*), interactive white boards and other online facilities such as virtual field trips and collaborative writing platforms.

Educational technologies have frequently been promoted as a panacea for student engagement, but there has also been an alarming gap between claims about what using new technologies can achieve and clear evidence of enhanced teaching and learning. This chapter explores resources that primary school science teachers and children can use. It presents a theoretical framework that can inform the use of existing and emerging digital educational technologies, or what we refer to as *learning technologies*. Throughout this chapter, we refer to specific examples of technologies including apps and websites. It is important to note that these are current examples of high-quality resources and new ones are constantly in development. Key online resources are superscripted in the text and listed at the end of the chapter.

The learning technologies landscape

Learning technologies may include hardware such as laptops and game consoles, peripherals such as wearable devices and software such as educational games and simulations. A wide range of discipline-specific and generic educational software and apps can be used to support children's science learning. Science-specific applications include data collection apps, visualisations, animations and participatory simulations, which might actively immerse children in realistic scientist roles or support rich experiences of authentic, community-based science projects. For example, *nQuire* allows upper primary school science learners to join a scientific mission that might involve a science experiment or data gathering using a mobile device. The *Scistarter* website advertises a range of community science projects that may be of interest to children. Apps such as *iSpot*, *Frog Spotter* and the *Platypus Spot* focus on learning about the natural environment, enabling children to participate in ongoing, collaborative research and conservation projects. Other examples of science-specific applications include simulations, such as *Google Sky* or those available in the elementary section of the *PhET* site, that allow children to explore more time-consuming or difficult to set up science scenarios. Effective science-specific software programs and apps position children in relevant, stimulating science activities that enable collaborative participation in meaningful science inquiry projects.

Other types of educational software and apps are more general purpose and can be used in any curriculum area to support learning.

Figure 8.1 Web-based learning technologies (from Bower & Torrington, 2020, p. 2. Used with permission).

For example, Bower and Torrington (2020) categorised free online learning technologies that can be used to support content creation, social connectivity and interactive learning. Their typology is shown in Figure 8.1 and consists of a range of web-based learning technologies.

A good way to examine the wide learning technologies landscape is to consider *how* devices and specific apps might be used by teachers and learners, and for what educational purpose. In this way, teachers can go beyond shallow discussions centred on the technical attributes and aesthetics of new technologies to critically consider how these digital tools might be used in ways that benefit children's learning. Revisiting the general-purpose case of online applications and the groupings of tools in Figure 8.1, collaborative mind-mapping tools (image-based tools cluster) could allow groups of children to engage in concept mapping, for example, to elicit prior knowledge and provide feedback to teachers. Some tools in Figure 8.1, such as blogs, wikis or other website creation tools, can be used to support students' reflection and authentic assessment for learning (see Chapter 7) through digital portfolios, or they could be used for digital storytelling and expression or peer collaboration. We present illustrations showing *how* other learning technologies might be used in science education for various pedagogical purposes in the snapshots later in this chapter.

A challenge for primary school science teachers is to evaluate and select high-quality learning resources, both generic and science-specific, for example, from the thousands of apps in the education categories in the Apple App or Google Play stores. The majority of apps in these repositories are shallow, rote learning apps, simply designed to provide information or opportunities for drill-and-practice (Bano et al., 2018). This can make it difficult for primary school teachers to find more creative apps that support participative, socially interactive approaches and potentially leverage more meaningful learning (see Chapters 2 and 3). Indeed, the US Office of Educational Technology (2017) warns of a new *digital use divide* between 'students who use technology to create, design, build, explore and collaborate, and those who simply use technology to consume media passively' (p. 18). Fortunately, there are resources to assist with the challenges, including various rubrics[1] for critically examining apps. Some rubrics focus on the potential use of apps to support teaching approaches, including one that is specifically designed to evaluate science apps (Green et al., 2014), and another rubric[2] that helps teachers evaluate the mobile pedagogical value of apps.

Teaching and learning primary school science with technology

Planning primary school science learning tasks involves many decisions about the learning outcomes, possible learning technologies and how children might use them to optimise learning. Some of the resources and associated teaching and learning strategies are science-specific and thus science teachers need to draw these together with their pedagogical expertise. Availability of different kinds of software and hardware tools will vary considerably by school and the socio-economic background of students as will both technical support and internet access, so it is important to consider contextual variables and to understand the pedagogical purposes as well as affordances and limitations in decision-making and planning.

Digital pedagogy

The term *digital pedagogy* describes the art of teaching and learning with contemporary learning technologies. The broad categories of these technologies introduced earlier offer a starting place to consider how the use of technology might mediate science learning. However, primary school science teachers need a theory of learning to drive their digital pedagogical decision-making and planning. In the contemporary context where high-quality digital resources are readily available, teachers are expected to go beyond presentational approaches, such as using the interactive whiteboard for demonstrations, to more progressive approaches that promote children's agency in their learning, such as student-generated media projects.

For many years, behaviourism has been the dominant learning theory influencing the design and use of learning technologies. Early technologies such as Skinner's teaching machine[3] in the 1950s and 1960s and technologies such as the overhead projector, instructional television and videos in the 1970s were typically associated with didactic, lecture-style, broadcast modes of teaching. Although more frequently adopted in secondary schools, primary school teachers sometimes choose to adopt these types of approaches, such as when using YouTube, screencast apps or digital pens to present information to children. While behaviourist approaches are persistent in technology-mediated teaching and learning, education reformers in the past four decades advocate designs that give learners more agency through inquiry, analysis and problem-solving with digital technologies (also see Chapters 2 and 5). Professor Seymour Papert was a pioneer in this movement during the 1980s, and, like Professor David Jonassen in the 1990s, promoted constructivist theory to underpin the development of more open-ended, generative uses of learning technologies to support children's creativity and critical thinking. Critical thinking applications, or what Jonassen labelled *mindtools*, include concept maps for collaborative planning, spreadsheets for problem-solving and modelling and simulations for hypothesis testing. Papert's classic 1980 book titled *Mindstorms* and Jonassen's 1996 book titled *Computers in the Classroom: Mindtools for Critical Thinking* are highly recommended as introductions to contemporary student-centred, learner-as-designer digital pedagogies.

In this section, we aim to push beginning primary school teachers to think beyond the strong influence of behaviourism on teaching approaches with technology, including its significant influence on the design of alluring, glitzy but educationally shallow apps. We encourage primary school teachers to explore digital pedagogies through the lens of social constructivism (see Chapter 2) to emphasise learning science *with*, rather than *about* or *from*, digital technologies to enhance children's articulation, representation and exchange of ideas and meaning-making.

Social constructivism highlights the social dimension of science learning activities (see Chapter 2) and enables learners' use of digital technologies to enhance discussion, questioning and negotiation of meaning among peers and teachers.

Social constructivist digital pedagogies

Following social constructivist theory, pedagogies need to give children the opportunity to realise their own background knowledge, challenge alternative conceptions (see Chapter 3) and build new meanings through shared learning experiences. An emphasis on the social aspects of learning means that experiences need to be planned so that learners have autonomy as they build collective knowledge both in the learning process and through the artefacts they produce. This positions teachers as consultants and monitors of children's learning and supporting these experiences with digital technologies then opens a range of possibilities to help children develop their science content knowledge and skills. Snapshots 8.1, 8.2 and 8.3 describe pedagogical approaches driven by a social constructivist theory of learning and depict children's use of contemporary learning technologies to meaningfully support collaborative learning.

Developing your science digital pedagogical knowledge

This chapter cannot begin to cover all of the possible digital resources that primary school teachers can use to effectively teach science. However, through initial teacher education programs and career-long professional development, beginning teachers will develop a variety of approaches to creatively exploit different technologies. Fortunately, there are many ways to keep current with new and emerging learning technologies and associated digital pedagogies. Well-known education bloggers such as Kathy Schrock[8] and Richard Byrne[9] help teachers keep current with an ever-growing list of learning technologies and digital teaching approaches. There are many professional organisations, such as the Australian Council for Computers in Education (ACCE) and the International Society for Technology in Education (ISTE) in the United States that produce pertinent publications and other resources for teacher professional development. The Australian Science Teachers' Association (ASTA) and

SNAPSHOT 8.1: Technology-supported science learning procedures

A straightforward way to use technology in designing constructivist-based science teaching is through the well-known science teaching procedure of Predict–Observe–Explain (POE). The purpose of a POE activity can range from eliciting children's pre-instructional science understandings, possibly provoking cognitive conflict, where their beliefs and what they observe do not match, to a more deliberate strategy designed to support students' meaning-making. Technology can assist in the prediction and observation phases. To provoke the *predict* phase of the POE, a short video stimulus from YouTube Kids, such as a snippet of a dangerous, time-consuming or expensive demonstration, could be presented for learners to consider a scenario, before using the video controls (slow motion, rewind etc.) to scrutinise the outcome. Close observation of the science phenomenon can provoke peer discussion leading into the explain phase. Data loggers or apps can be used during the observation phase, for instance, to measure someone's heart rate or the pitch of a sound.

Importantly, technology can be used to guide pairs or small groups of learners through the POE procedure and facilitate more autonomous, collaborative learning (Kearney, 2004). Online interactive video platforms such as *Edpuzzle* or even a carefully planned sequence of *Google Slides* can be used to scaffold children's engagement in each step of a POE task and allow them to exchange ideas and progress at their own pace. Digital technology can also support the seamless collection and collation of students' responses in each phase of the POE process to inform later instruction. Importantly, children's responses may provide insights into their alternative conceptions and provoke additional questions as new points of interest. Thus, children's questioning, verbal or written, during a POE can lead discussions in many new directions. Templates and examples for designing a technology-supported POE activity and sparking ideas are available from the Learning Designs site.[4] Indeed, upper level primary school students can create their own POE task to share with their peers. Other reference materials, such as procedures available from the Project for Enhancing Effective Learning (PEEL),[5] offer robust, research-based ways to design learning activities that can be readily adapted for use with digital technologies.

SNAPSHOT 8.2: Inquiry-based science learning

As developed in Chapter 6, inquiry as a teaching approach gives children the opportunity to explore a question of interest to them. Curriculum scholars have developed several inquiry frameworks, but Bybee's 5E model is among the most popular. There are particular focal points for each of the Es (Engage, Explore, Explain, Elaborate, Evaluate) and working through each of these stages mirrors the work of scientists in conducting an inquiry that can be supported with various technologies. For example, a 5E inquiry could focus on a community science project investigating local fauna. Here, students could use their mobile devices during the early phases of the inquiry to explore the phenomenon and generate areas of interest and project goals. In a similar way to real scientists, students can use apps to communicate in real-time, collect data in situ and co-author and share findings. Teachers can arrange to have children liaise with an expert biologist-in-residence in a real-time video chat to discuss the project goals and seek guidance for data collection procedures. In later stages of the inquiry, children could travel to different local areas, collecting multimodal artefacts in the field, including photos and videos and make annotated notes to share amongst themselves, the teacher and the biologist. As part of a team, the students in this scenario use password-protected online spaces such as the school's learning management system or a class blog, to pose questions and share their predictions and interpretations with peers doing similar projects in other local or more distant neighbourhoods, or with other scientific experts. In this way, the mobile learning activity enables the children to think and behave as part of a real scientific community and act as co-constructors of knowledge through authentic activity. Sharing materials in a safe online space means that the biologist also has access to their shared notes and real-time data and can quickly give feedback. The students can then co-write a brief report in an online collaborative document and share their findings with the science community in the Elaborate and Evaluate phases.

SNAPSHOT 8.3: Digital explanation

A design-based example of a digital learning experience for primary school science students is student-generated digital media or *digital explanation* where children develop an explanation of a science concept for a specified audience. For example, children can generate an animation to represent conceptual knowledge or interpretations of dynamic relationships such as forces. Movie-making programs such as iMovie allow easy upload of still images, video and other digital media forms and support development of a progressive sequence of representations that can be edited and narrated to make a mini-movie to explain the science concept to others. Other software or apps allow children to easily create animations, or slow-motion animations (see the Slowmation[6] and Digiexplanation[7] sites). Developing an explanation of a science concept for others is a highly effective way for children to learn science content because to explain something, they need to understand it. So, in creating a digital explanation, children consider the science content, choose what will be represented and how, and then work with a range of digital tools to communicate their science understandings. These short, stand-alone mini-movies can be engaging as a task, allowing children to work with science content in an open-ended way that is well-suited to groups and collaborations. The process of developing a digital explanation can also help children to develop new media skills and digital literacies because they both learn from and produce multiple representations while working to produce an accurate explanation. Research in this area has productively demonstrated the value for a range of science learners, including preservice teachers (Hoban, Nielsen & Shepherd, 2013).

state-level science teachers' associations hold annual conferences that offer networking opportunities to share and discuss innovations in teaching, including emerging digital pedagogies in science. Attending teacher conferences and developing a professional learning network (or PLN) incorporating links with other teachers and organisations, both locally and globally, serve to connect teachers to others interested in similar questions of teaching and learning. For example, many teachers attend TeachMeets and then use social media to continue their professional learning conversations in spaces such as Twitter (e.g., using #PrimarySTEMchat, #ozscied and #aussied memes) and Facebook.

Learning spaces for primary school science

Primary school teachers should also consider the growing range of physical and online contemporary learning spaces when designing technology-mediated learning tasks and enacting digital pedagogies. Formal physical spaces may include classrooms and school libraries, while virtual spaces may include structured class blogs or school learning management systems. Semi-formal physical spaces may include school playgrounds, break-out spaces and excursion sites such as science museums, while semi-formal online spaces could include science chat sites, other online communities or virtual tours and field trips, for example, *Google Expeditions*. In these formal and semi-formal spaces, children's learning experiences are typically designed and mediated by a teacher or external expert such as a museum tour guide.

With the availability of mobile devices and accompanying educational apps, there is a growing range of informal learning spaces where children can learn science. For primary school aged children, these spaces could include buses, shopping centres and spaces at home, all of which are appealing because the spaces are typically more convenient and intimate for learners. Informal virtual learning environments can be connective, participative spaces for upper level primary school children, such as tween-friendly social media networks and immersive online worlds that can be accessed using mobile tools anywhere and anytime. Designing science learning activities that utilise these physical and virtual learning spaces, some of which are learner-generated and therefore unpredictable, is a new and exciting challenge for primary school teachers.

Children are increasingly comfortable moving and learning across multiple learning spaces—formal and informal—for example, when carrying out citizen science projects. Some educators describe this boundary-crossing between learning spaces as *seamless learning*, for example connecting learning in classrooms and science museums, or providing a bridge between classroom-based inquiry and more realistic, in situ collection of data from a beach or forest. Mobile devices and associated learning technologies can mediate this flow of learning between formal and informal contexts, for example, through children's use of online role playing or cloud-based applications such as *Google Sheets*.

A few caveats

A chapter on using digital technology to support science learning would be incomplete without a few caveats. Factors affecting technology use in schools will continue to evolve and shape the digital education landscape in primary school science teaching and learning.

Enablers and barriers to integration of technology in primary school science teaching

Both enablers and barriers of digital technology adoption and integration in schools have been well documented. First-order factors include access to technology, school budgets, technical administration and support, as well as time for planning and professional development. Second-order factors are more critical and include teacher beliefs, digital competencies and pedagogical approaches (Ertmer et al., 2012). Teachers' pedagogical beliefs are perhaps the most critical influence on the way learning technologies are used in and beyond the primary school classroom. If teachers have behaviourist beliefs, they tend to use educational technologies that support didactic, transmissive teaching approaches, for example, using PowerPoint to *teach by telling*, or an interactive whiteboard in a presentation style to transfer information. This may promote rote learning. In contrast, teachers with social constructivist beliefs will design more student-centred, collaborative, expressive and creative technology-enhanced science learning tasks. Notably, such constructivist approaches are consistent with contemporary directions in both learning theory and curriculum and provide extensive opportunity to utilise learning technologies in generative and engaging ways.

Drivers of technology in primary school education

Many learning technologies, such as interactive whiteboards and laptops, have been introduced into schools via a *top down* approach under the influence of external bodies such as governments and powerful corporations such as Google, Microsoft and Apple. An economic rationale is typically central to arguments driving investment, for example, to prepare students with 21st-century skills that are relevant in a rapidly changing global economy and for future workplaces. An example from state-level government is the 2011 NSW Connected Classroom program that spent $23 million on 4300 interactive whiteboards for classrooms.

Professional organisations, regulatory agencies and curriculum designers are also influential. The Commonwealth Government in Australia recently instituted regulations in the form of the Australian Professional Standards for Teachers (APST, Australian Curriculum, Assessment and Reporting Authority [ACARA], 2013), with three standards addressing the effective and safe use of technology for teaching: Standards 2.6, 3.4 and 4.5. (See Illustrations of Practice for these standards via the AITSL website[10]). The General Capabilities section of the Australian Curriculum (ACARA, 2020) explicitly states students should develop ICT capability and use it to develop conceptual understandings, research science concepts and communicate findings. The Technologies learning area curriculum also specifies a range of skills and knowledge for learning about and working with technology.

More recently, the use of learning technologies such as cloud-based software (e.g., Google Documents), digital video editing software and many education apps have been introduced and promoted in schools. Arguably these more *bottom up* strategies have had greater impact because they are under the influence of smaller scale, localised drivers such as pioneering teachers and school leaders, parents, local authorities or school systems. For instance, more locally developed school-based laptop or Bring Your Own Device (BYOD) policies can positively influence practices and children's access to technology.

Summary of key points

Teachers' beliefs about teaching and learning critically influence the way that educational technologies are used by children in learning science. Social constructivism is a useful theory for beginning teachers to develop digital pedagogies that emphasise students' learning *with* technologies to support discussion and exchange of ideas, open-ended questioning and co-construction of meaning. Collaborative technology-supported design and inquiry-based activities are highly suitable for these purposes. Teachers also need to think about where and when science learning might take place and how the use of mobile technologies and associated apps might leverage new physical and virtual learning spaces for science students to think, co-create and investigate.

Discussion questions

7.1. Where do you need to focus your own professional learning to develop your repertoire of digital pedagogies? How could your professional learning network (PLN) help you?

7.2. You are teaching in a school with a *Bring Your Own Device* (BYOD) policy. Design a science learning activity that exploits the *anywhere, anytime, any pace* flexibility of learning with a mobile device. How could the notion of *seamless learning* across contexts inform your design? Use this short YouTube video[11] as a stimulus for your planning.

7.3. Use one or more of the evaluation rubrics flagged in this chapter to compare and contrast two of your favourite science learning apps for children.

7.4. Use a constructivist perspective to inform the design and implementation of a science activity for children that exploits the use of one or more carefully selected education apps. Evaluate your activity using the teacher and student versions of these validated surveys.[12]

7.5. Video-based examples of science lessons informed by a constructivist perspective are available at the University of South Florida's well-known Technology Integration Matrix (TIMS).[13] Choose and view an F-6 science example that is tagged 'Collaborative'. How is peer collaboration supporting student learning in the lesson?

Resources

Resources 1–13 from this chapter can also be accessed online at: https://bit.ly/nielsenkearneyresources.

1. https://www.schrockguide.net/assessment-and-rubrics.html
2. http://www.mobilelearningtoolkit.com/app-rubric1.html
3. https://youtu.be/jTH3ob1IRFo
4. http://www.learningdesigns.uow.edu.au/index.html
5. http://www.peelweb.org/
6. http://www.slowmation.com/

7. http://www.digiexplanations.com
8. http://www.schrockguide.net/
9. http://www.freetech4teachers.com/.
10. https://www.aitsl.edu.au/tools-resources
11. https://youtu.be/9zxlZvJ-3Aw
12. https://www.ipacmobilepedagogy.com/
13. https://fcit.usf.edu/matrix/matrix/subject-area-index/

References

Australian Curriculum, Assessment and Reporting Authority (ACARA). (2013). *Australian professional standards for teachers*. Sydney: Author.

Australian Curriculum, Assessment and Reporting Authority (ACARA). (2020). *Australian Curriculum*. Accessed September 28 2020 at: https://www.australiancurriculum.edu.au/f-10-curriculum/general-capabilities/.

Bano, M., Zowghi, D., Kearney, M., Schuck, S., & Aubusson, P. (2018). Mobile learning for science and mathematics school education: A systematic review of empirical evidence. *Computers & Education, 121*, 30–58. https://doi.org/10.1016/j.compedu.2018.02.006.

Bower, M., & Torrington, J. (2020). *A typology of free web-based learning technologies*. EDUCAUSE digital library. Accessed May 14 2020 at: https://library.educause.edu//media/files/library/2020/4/freewebbasedlearntech2020.pdf.

Ertmer, P. A., Ottenbreit-Leftwich, A. T., Sadik, O., Sendurur, E., & Sendurur, P. (2012). Teacher beliefs and technology integration practices: A critical relationship. *Computers and Education, 59*, 423–435.

Green, L. S., Hechter, R. P., Tysinger, P. D., & Chassereau, K. D. (2014). Mobile app selection for 5th through 12th grade science: The development of the MASS rubric. *Computers and Education, 75*, 65–71.

Hoban, G., Nielsen, W., & Shepherd, A. (2013). Explaining and communicating science using student-created blended media. *Teaching Science: Australian Science Teachers Journal, 59*(1), 32–35.

Jonassen, D. H. (1996). *Computers in the classroom: Mindtools for critical thinking*. Columbus, OH: Merrill/PrenticeHall.

Kearney, M. (2004). Classroom use of multimedia supported predict-observe-explain tasks in a social constructivist learning environment. *Research in Science Education, 34*(4), 427–453.

Office of Educational Technology. (2017). *Reimagining the role of technology in education: 2017 National Education Technology Plan update*. US Department of Education. Accessed July 17 2020 at: https://tech.ed.gov/files/2017/01/NETP17.pdf.

Papert, S. (1980). *Mindstorms*. New York, NY: Basic Books.

9

PROJECT- AND PROBLEM-BASED LEARNING AND LEARNING OUTSIDE OF THE CLASSROOM

Kimberley Pressick-Kilborn

Goals

The goals for this chapter are to support you to:

- Plan for student learning through understanding the key features of project-based and problem-based approaches to primary school science teaching
- Be familiar with wide-ranging opportunities for student learning outside the classroom
- Consider practical issues and class management when using advanced teaching strategies

Australian Professional Standards for Teachers—Graduate Level:

- Standard 2: Know the content and how to teach it (Focus area 2.2)
- Standard 3: Plan for and implement effective teaching and learning (3.2, 3.3, 3.4)
- Standard 4: Create and maintain supportive and safe learning environments (4.1, 4.2, 4.4)
- Standard 7: Engage professionally with colleagues, parents/carers and the community (focus area 7.4)

Introduction

As primary school science teachers, when we situate our students' learning in the world around them (Snapshot 9.1), we help to create meaning and purpose and to promote opportunities for genuine engagement. Students' conceptual science learning can be related to everyday activities, and skills can be learnt and applied in relevant contexts. In this chapter, you will be introduced to approaches to teaching that embed students' science learning in their local communities and beyond. Two active, student-centred inquiry approaches that both (sometimes confusingly!) use the acronym *PBL* will be featured and distinguished: *project-based learning* and *problem-based learning*. Particular focus will then be given to science learning outside the classroom, including both excursions and incursions. Throughout the chapter, practical issues will be considered and class management tips will be shared, so that you can plan for using advanced teaching strategies with confidence.

SNAPSHOT 9.1: *Students' interest and science learning*

As the Year 1 students came into the classroom after lunch break, two students excitedly approached Ms Lee. Inside their lunchboxes, they had collected a number of seedpods that had fallen from *Banksia* trees in the playground (Figure 9.1). As Ms Lee settled the class in a circle on the floor, she invited the two students to pass the seedpods around to their classmates. She asked the students to closely look at the seedpods and encouraged them to talk with their peers in the circle about what they noticed. How were they similar? How were they different? Ms Lee overheard lots of curious voices in the groups as students expressed their thoughts and interest. Then one of the students asked if he could get a magnifying glass from the science storage trays in their classroom, and another student asked if she could take some photographs on a class tablet device to add to their weekly class blog that was shared with parents. Ms Lee looked around the classroom at her students, who were examining and talking animatedly about the seedpods. She wondered what she could do next to capitalise on the students' interest and wonder and to build on this opportunity for science learning?

Project-based learning

Project-based learning has become a popular approach in all education sectors—primary, secondary and tertiary—as teachers seek to design more authentic and personalised learning experiences for students. It differs from simply *doing* a project, which can be unfocused and unfiltered. For example, *doing* a project may simply involve students making a poster that includes all they can find about pelicans, copying and pasting large chunks of information without purpose or comprehension. In contrast, project-based learning focuses on supporting students to develop skills that they need to become independent learners, to locate

Figure 9.1 (a) *Banksia* trees and flowers. (b) *Banksia* seed pods.

Figure 9.1 (Continued)

and build knowledge through sustained engagement to achieve a specific goal. In primary school science, established citizen science projects such as *StreamWatch* (https://www.streamwatch.org.au/) or *Birds in Schools* (http://birdlife.org.au/projects/urban-birds/birds-in-schools-project) could provide contexts for more externally guided project-based learning (refer also to Chapter 13 on environmental education).

Key features of project-based learning

Project-based learning is characterised by its student-driven nature, with investigation characterising the process, resulting in creation of a tangible product (Strevy, 2014). The teacher's sound knowledge of the curriculum is vital, as students address curriculum outcomes through engagement in project-based learning, rather than students doing a project as an add-on or a homework task. The timeframe may be as short as a week, with many lessons dedicated to the project within that short period, or as long as a school term. In the process of project-based learning, there is usually incorporation of suitable digital platforms and applications to support the learning (see Chapter 8).

Although there are a number of models of project-based learning, there are key features across all of these models that distinguish this approach (Buck Institute for Education, nd; Maher & Yoo, 2017):

- *Driving question*—The driving or *essential* question provides a starting point for inquiry and focuses the project. The question should be sufficiently open and suitably complex, so that it can be responded to or pursued in a number of ways. With younger students, the question may be decided by the teacher in advance or negotiated with the students. With older students, the driving question could be negotiated collaboratively as a class, or decided individually or in small groups, with guidance in framing a suitable question provided by the teacher. The driving question should have *real life* significance in that it is meaningful beyond the classroom. It should be of interest and relevance to the students and provide a *hook* for them to engage with curiosity in learning. Examples of driving questions to guide primary school science learning include *What is the impact of introduced species in native Australian ecosystems?* or *How have sporting materials changed over time to enhance human performance?* Using the latter question, students could choose a particular sport as their focus, and their investigations could include fair tests with different materials, interviews with sports people, guest speaker presentations from sports scientists, a visit to a sports museum and research in books and on websites.

- *A product of the project is created, to address the question*—In the process of learning through the project, students are actively involved in creating a tangible product that reflects the knowledge and skills they have developed. The product could take a range of forms, including written or oral reports, labelled diagrams, posters, library displays, newspaper articles, podcast episodes, video documentaries or short films, assembly presentations, portfolios, animations, blog or vlog posts, models, board games, a workshop for peers or plays. Products can be individual or group creations. In some project-based learning units, the teacher might specify the required form of the product, although students' inquiries may take different pathways. An advantage of all students creating the same form is that common lessons can then be planned to support them in developing skills to be able to create that product. Different product forms may be more suited to younger or older students, or the content focus of particular projects.

- *Regular assessment and feedback*—During the process of project-based learning, regular informal, formative assessment of students' progress in their learning is provided by the teacher, from peers and parents. Students' self-reflection and self-assessment, whether individual or in relation to group tasks, is also frequently incorporated. As the teacher takes the important role of actively guiding student learning in projects, one aspect is providing constructive and timely feedback for students. The final products created can be assessed in a variety of ways, which could include rubrics that include criteria and descriptors of success that have been negotiated with students at the outset of the project (see Chapter 7).

- *Authentic audience*—The products created in project-based approaches are shared with an authentic audience. The audience could include students from another class or year group, or from another school (either in real life or virtually via video-conferencing), parents and carers, community members or distinguished guests such as the local mayor. A special event can be planned for sharing learning products, such as a conference or summit, exhibition or showcase, festival or forum. The event can take place at school, or in local venues such as community halls, public libraries, local museums or even parks. The suitability of the event location can be decided depending on the focus of the projects and the products created. Snapshot 9.2 provides an example of PBL.

Strengths and challenges of project-based learning

One of the strengths in taking a project-based approach is that it can support opportunities for differentiated and personalised learning and

SNAPSHOT 9.2: How can we reduce waste in our school?

Ms Poulos had decided to involve her Year 6 students in a project-based learning unit, with a view to addressing the Science as a Human Endeavour strand in the Australian Curriculum: *Science* (Australian Curriculum, Assessment and Reporting Authority [ACARA], 2020). As a provocation to arouse student curiosity and interest, she showed students a segment from the ABC documentary, *War on Waste* (https://iview.abc.net.au/show/war-on-waste). This led to small group discussions about students' own home and school waste generation and disposal, and the associated environmental impact of their choices. The students re-gathered as a class to share their small group observations. Ms Poulos asked her students whether they thought changes could be made and in what ways? She shared her plan for them to engage in project-based science learning, and by the end of the lesson, there was agreement reached on a driving focus question: *How can we reduce waste in our school?* Ms Poulos had designed the framework for the unit such that students had relatively open choice in how they would address this question through devising and conducting individual projects designed to investigate the issue of waste reduction and management. However, she did narrow down students' choice of possible products by deciding the form in which the projects would be presented. Ms Poulos said that in the final weeks of the term, the students would need to form small *action groups*. Using the collective findings from their respective individual projects, each action group would need to develop a proposal for a waste reduction initiative to present to the principal and the Student Representative Council (SRC) members for consideration. With input from the principal and approval from the SRC, the Year 6 students would then put these initiatives in place in the following term, with funding support already agreed to from the school's Parents' and Citizens' Association.

teaching, to cater for the diverse needs and interests of students in any class. The nature of project-based approaches promotes a sense of student ownership of learning, with development of skills and dispositions relating to self-direction, planning, time management, goal-setting, decision-making and responsibility. Students can work at a varied pace and on different activities that contribute to their project. Guidance and feedback from the teacher can support all students in experiencing a sense of challenge in their learning.

There are potential challenges to consider, before you use a project-based approach:

- *Role of the teacher:* In a project-based learning classroom, often you will feel like the conductor of an orchestra! You will need to feel comfortable with *just-in-time* teaching for when it becomes clear to you that students need to develop specific skills or knowledge to take the next step in their project.
- *Class management:* Students working on a range of different projects at the same time can be difficult to manage. Plan to have lesson introduction time where you bring the class together with a common focus, and end lessons with a reflective class circle discussion to spotlight progress as well as share any difficulties encounter.
- *Ensuring a clear focus on science concepts and skills:* Project-based learning often is designed to be multidisciplinary, so when science is one of the integrated STEM subjects (see Chapters 11 and 12), it is important to maintain a focus on particular knowledge, understandings and skills specific to science.

Problem-based learning

Problem-based learning is an inquiry process that engages students in developing solutions that address complex or *fuzzy* real-world problems or scenarios (Strevy, 2014). Problem-based learning starts with a problem to be solved, and in science, learning could include local, national or global problems. For example, starting points could be larger scale problems such as an oil spill and clean up, plastic waste in oceans or habitat loss resulting from land clearing. Problems that derive from students' immediate personal experiences, such as crying when you cut onions or wanting to know whether you can make chocolate powder dissolve more quickly in milk, could also be potential starting points. Like project-based learning, the problems posed should have multiple possible solutions, as real world problems are unlikely to have clear, neat or simple answers. Problem-based learning does not always take as long as project-based learning because students develop and present a solution, which can take a few hours, or a few weeks, depending on the nature of the problem. As such, problem-based learning can be embedded as an approach within a term-long lesson sequence, as part of a broader teaching and learning unit. Often, problem-based learning is collaborative, with students working in pairs or small groups.

Key features of problem-based learning

- *Defining the problem:* Learning is initiated with a problem. Decisions to make when deciding on a suitable problem for the focus of learning include whether the problem will be one that is teacher-located and shared, or collaboratively identified by the teacher and students, or student-generated.
- *Dealing with relevant information:* The problem-based learning process involves students identifying what is already known (prior knowledge) and what needs to be known to develop a solution. Students then locate relevant information sources and resources (for example, community members, experts) or ways of finding out (for example, through science inquiry or fair testing as a process of investigation).
- *Negotiating and allocating roles:* Students will need time and guidance in planning how to find out what needs to be known. Teacher support could include providing decision-making frameworks and establishing shared processes for resolving any conflict that may arise.
- *Developing a solution and communicating it:* Once relevant information has been found or developed, students need to apply it to generate a solution to the problem. This requires creative thinking and problem-solving. Feedback from the teacher and others, as well as self- or group-reflection, will likely result in revisions to their solution, prior to presenting it.

Snapshot 9.3 provides an example of problem-based learning.

SNAPSHOT 9.3: The hot slippery dip slide

Mr Baker's Year 3 class was learning about heat production and heat transfer in their Term 1 science unit, *Science understanding* strand, physical sciences sub-strand (ACARA, 2020). He decided to begin the unit using a problem-based learning scenario. In the lesson before lunch, Mr Baker took the students to the playground in the park across the road from the school. In the midday sun, the metal slippery dip slide was hot to touch. The students took turns in feeling it, and then Mr Baker asked them whether anyone wanted to slide down. They all agreed that it was too hot to be fun! When they returned to the classroom, Mr Baker wrote on the board '*Problem*: The slippery dip slide is too hot to slide down on sunny days.' He asked the students individually to think about how this problem could be solved, then gave them time to discuss their initial ideas in table groups. There were six table groups each with four students. After lunch, in larger groups of eight, the students were given time to share initial thinking, then develop and refine an idea that they agreed would be interesting to pursue as a solution. Mr Baker gave each large group a planning template to use, to collaboratively develop a focus for an investigation to present to the class. This reduced the number of different concurrent investigations to three, which Mr Baker believed was manageable. The different groups proposed:

1.   A shade cover: What would make the best material to shade the slide but not make the playground too shady and dark? What would be the best shaped design for the cover? This group planned to do some fair testing, and design and make a model.
2.   Different slide material: Is there a better material for the slide itself to be made from? This group discussed two essential qualities: the material needs to be adequately slippery for sliding, but also needs to stay relatively cool when it is in sunshine. This group planned to conduct fair tests and to look up websites to see what materials playground manufacturers use for making slippery dips.

3. Using a sack for sliding: What would be the best material to make a sack from, so that it wasn't too slippery but protected bare legs from the heat of the slippery dip? This group planned to engage in fair testing, as well as designing and making a prototype sack.

With the three proposals shared, Mr Baker asked the students to form pairs. He asked each pair to choose one of the three investigations and submit their choice to him. At the end of the day, he was able to make plans for the resourcing and organisation of materials for the subsequent science lessons to accommodate the students' choices.

Strengths and challenges of problem-based learning

A key strength of problem-based learning is that it provides a rich context for student-led inquiry, which can include fair tests and other forms of scientific investigation as shown in the slippery dip snapshot. It can be motivating for students to be solving real problems, and empowering for them to apply inquiry skills and the practices of science, such as openness to ideas, to develop reasoned solutions. Engagement in real local or global problems can support students to develop new perspectives about the world in which they live and provide experiences of agency for making positive and evidence-based change. A further strength of problem-based learning is that solving a problem provides opportunities for science argumentation (Naylor, Keogh & Dowling, 2007), as students evaluate sources and evidence, debate possible solutions, provide reasons for their thinking and justify their final solution to others.

Potential challenges to consider, before you use a problem-based approach include:

- *Identifying a suitable problem:* It can be difficult to frame an ill-defined problem to present to primary-aged students, which may lead to posing a simulated rather than real-world problem. Initially, teachers can collaborate with colleagues in scenario generation. As students become more experienced with problem-based approach, they can take greater responsibility for identifying problems and planning for solving the problem.

- *Class management:* Similar to project-based learning, the ideal in problem-based learning is for students to direct or lead the process, with the teacher actively supporting and shaping the learning. When students are not experienced with problem-based learning, modelling can help. Modelling involves proceeding through the steps of the problem-based approach as a whole class, highly scaffolded by the teacher, with the focus on a single common problem. In small groups, students work on developing different solutions.

Learning outside of the classroom

One of the greatest things about teaching primary school science is that there are endless possibilities for students to learn outside the classroom, as well as bringing the world beyond the classroom into students' learning. In doing so, we not only bring science to life but create opportunities to build partnerships with parents, carers and the community more widely (Coleman et al., 2019; Department of Education, Skills and Employment, 2019).

Taking students outside the classroom

When you think back to your own primary school days, excursions and field trips are possibly some of the most memorable experiences. Engaging and exciting sites for science excursions include zoos, museums and science centres, environmental education centres, aquaria, observatories, national parks and nature reserves, botanic gardens, farms and theme parks. Locally to your school, no doubt there are many free sites for science learning such as parks, local rivers, wetlands and lakes, beaches, and public buildings and bridges. Even the school playground presents numerous opportunities for learning science.

Research in Australia in the 1990s led to the development of a teaching/learning framework called *SMILES (School-Museum Integrated Learning Experiences for Students)* (Griffin, 1996). This research established that key to effective site visits is not just the strategies that teachers use at the site, but the suite of learning provided before, during and after the visit. Primary school-aged students achieve extensive learning through excursions and field trips when they:

- know the purpose of the visit,
- have some control over their learning,

- have choice about what, where and how they learn,
- work with small groups.

While your own memory of school excursions might include completing worksheets during a *day off* the regular routine of school, the *SMILES* framework emphasises the importance of students having choice at the site. Activities at the site will be linked with ongoing investigations that the students are engaged in at school. In advance of the visit, students should know what they will do with the documentation made during the visit, when they return to school and their investigations continue and culminate.

Planning excursions involves risk and safety considerations, as well as necessary documentation including parent/carer permissions, and your local education authority or department will have guidelines to assist you. In primary schools, it is common practice to invite parents or education assistants as helpers to supervise students on excursions. It is always advisable to brief parents in advance on the learning purpose of the excursion and the specific ways that parent helpers can support students' learning on the day. As a teacher, you should visit the site in advance, prior to the class excursion, so that you are familiar with the opportunities for learning as well as the layout and other features of the site, so that you also can plan for class management in advance.

Bringing the outside into the classroom

One way that primary school teachers often bring the outside into the classroom is by creating classroom displays of science topic-related objects and materials. For example, in one Foundation classroom, the teacher and students had brought into school a range of artefacts relating to living things that they had found or that they owned. The display was built up over the term, and during both science lessons and free play, the students were encouraged to engage with it. Alternative resources for classroom displays and other learning activities can be sourced through outreach programs such as the Australian Museum's *Museum in a Box* (https://australianmuseum.net.au/learn/teachers/museum-box/). The program provides loans of items including real museum specimens, casts and teachers' notes to educational institutions across Australia. A range of themed boxes has been curated for loan.

Other ways of bringing the outside into the classroom or school include *incursions*, where an external organisation, people, activities or artefacts visit the class. Possible incursions could involve mobile planetariums, native wildlife displays or expert guest speakers from your school's parent community, Indigenous community elders or scientists working in local organisations. Additionally, connections with scientists can be formed through programs such as the CSIRO Education's *STEM Professionals in Schools* (https://education.csiro.au). Video-conferencing opens up a range of possibilities for guest speakers from beyond your local community, and for building connections in science teaching and learning with students and teachers in other schools nationally and internationally.

Summary of key points

In this chapter, you have been introduced to some advanced strategies for teaching primary school science. Project-based learning, problem-based learning and learning outside of the classroom can be incorporated into your repertoire as a primary school science teacher. These approaches will actively engage students in meaningful, relevant and authentic contexts for learning. Emphasis in this chapter has been on student-led approaches to science inquiry, in which the teacher plays a vital guiding role, bringing knowledge of the curriculum to focus students on developing knowledge, understandings and skills specific to the discipline of science.

Discussion questions

9.1. Snapshot 9.1 ends in a question. What do *you* think Ms Lee could have done next? Brainstorm ideas for how a lesson sequence could be developed from this opportunity for science learning, initiated by the students. What links are there with other learning areas across the primary curriculum?

9.2. Have you had any previous experiences of either project-based learning or problem-based learning as a student yourself? During your professional experience placements, have you seen either PBL approach being used in primary classrooms? Describe the features of your own experiences or observations of PBL, and what you enjoyed, disliked or found interesting as a learner or observer.

9.3. In your own local area, what locations or organisations could make suitable excursion or field trip sites for primary science learning? Who might you contact in your local community as a guest speaker, presenter or expert collaborator when teaching primary science topics?

References

Australian Curriculum, Assessment and Reporting Authority (ACARA). (2020). *Australian Curriculum: Science* (scope and sequence of content). Accessed 11 June 2020 at: https://docs.acara.edu.au/resources/Science_-_Sequence_of_content.pdf.

Buck Institute for Education (nd). *PBLworks*. Accessed 11 June 2020 at: https://www.pblworks.org/.

Coleman, S., Chinn, P., Morrison, D., & Kaupp, L. (2019). How place-based science education strategies can support equity for students, teachers, and communities. STEM Teaching Tool #57. Accessed 11 June 2020 at: http://stemteachingtools.org/brief/57.

Department of Education, Skills and Employment. (2019). *Alice Springs (Mparntwe) Education Declaration*. Canberra: Australian Government. Accessed 11 June 2020 at: https://docs.education.gov.au/documents/alice-springs-mparntwe-education-declaration.

Griffin, J. (1996). *SMILES: School-museum informal learning experiences*. Sydney: University of Technology Sydney.

Maher, D., & Yoo, J. (2017). Project-based learning in the primary school classroom. *Progress in Education* (pp. 105–119), Volume 43.

Naylor, S., Keogh, B., & Dowling, B. (2007). Argumentation and primary science. *Research in Science Education*, 37(1), 17–39.

Strevy, D. (2014). Focus on teacher education: Project-based learning: Is there a problem-based difficulty? *Childhood Education*, 90(6), 462–465.

10

DIFFERENTIATED TEACHING PRACTICES AND STRATEGIES TO MEET DIVERSE STUDENT NEEDS

Kimberley Wilson and Vicki Thorpe

Goals

The goals for this chapter are to support you to:

- Understand the importance of meeting the diverse needs of all students to ensure equity and inclusion in science education
- Understand differentiated teaching practices and strategies to respond and cater to the needs of all students
- Explain three instructional strategies for differentiation

Australian Professional Standards for Teachers—Graduate Level:

- Standard 1: Know students and how they learn (Focus areas 1.1, 1.3, 1.4, 1.5, 1.6)
- Standard 4: Create and maintain supportive and safe learning environments (Focus area: 4.1)

Introduction

The purpose of this chapter is to provide background knowledge and some practical strategies relating to accommodating diversity in primary school science classrooms. Past experience within a *one-size-fits-all* approach to science education often leads preservice teachers to believe that this type of approach will be sufficient to meet their students' needs in science. This belief, however, tends to become rapidly unstuck when faced with the realities of the regular primary school classroom, as indicated in the sentiments expressed next by a preservice teacher after a practicum experience that didn't quite go to plan:

> For my last practicum experience, I was really prepared, I had all my resources ready for the age level, I went into the classroom and then I realised that students weren't all at that same level, many of them were still at stage one ... so my whole lesson I was trying to help them but it wasn't working because I was so focused on the curriculum and how I was going to teach the students but I didn't think about their needs and where they were at. I didn't assess that properly, so that's where that tension was for me.
>
> (Preservice primary school teacher).

It is not uncommon for preservice teachers to find there is a significant gap between what they learn about science education in their university preparation and the reality of ensuring all students develop appropriate science content knowledge and inquiry skills when many students are at different stages of cognitive, behavioural and social/emotional development. This chapter aims to help you to think about how you might best cater for diversity. You will need to do this to meet the Australian Professional Standards for Teachers that require all teachers to be able to 'differentiate teaching to meet the specific learning needs of students across the full range of abilities' (Australian Institute for Teaching and School Leadership [AITSL], 2011, p. 9).

Equity as a key education priority

The *Alice Springs (Mparntwe) Education Declaration* (Education Council, 2019) outlines a vision for Australian education that advocates for 'a world class education system that encourages and supports every student to be the very best they can be, no matter where they live or what kind of learning challenges they may face' (p. 2). This declaration details two distinct goals that need to be achieved for all Australian students to thrive in a rapidly changing social context. Goal 1 is particularly relevant to this chapter—'The Australian education system promotes excellence and equity'. Goal 2 highlights the importance of promoting educational conditions where 'All young Australians become: confident and creative individuals; successful lifelong learners and active and informed members of the community' (Education Council, 2019, p. 4). These goals are supported by the recent National School Reform Agreement (Department of Education and Training, 2018) that sets out long-term national goals for Australian school education. All Australian states and territories have agreed to the initiative to support 'existing and/or new reforms to lift outcomes for priority equity cohorts including Aboriginal and Torres Strait Islander students, students living in regional, rural and remote locations, students with a disability and students from educationally disadvantaged backgrounds' (p. 4).

The *Alice Springs (Mparntwe) Education Declaration* goals provide direction for the way in which the Australian Curriculum is designed and shaped to cater for the needs of all students. The Australian Curriculum makes clear that educational programs must recognise:

- that each student can learn and that the needs of every student are important,
- that each student is entitled to knowledge, understanding and skills that provide a foundation for successful and lifelong learning and participation in the Australian community,
- that high expectations should be set for each student,
- that the needs and interests of students will vary, and that schools and teachers should plan from the curriculum in ways that respond to those needs and interests (Australian Curriculum, Assessment and Reporting Authority [ACARA], 2020).

It is with these goals and curriculum expectations in mind that we as teachers of science need to demonstrate responsiveness in providing a rigorous, relevant and engaging learning program that addresses the individual learning needs of all students in our science classrooms.

Differentiation as a model of teaching practice

Differentiation is a research-based model of teaching practice that provides support for teachers to progress learning for all students in the classroom.

This model advocates that teachers need to be responsive to the diverse needs of all students with respect to differences in culture, language, experiences, economics or disability. The model recognises that students come to the classroom with a wide range of interests, experiences, family circumstances, support systems, maturity and confidence, academic readiness and social, emotional, cognitive and behavioural needs.

In differentiated classrooms, teachers know their students' interests and needs and manage student learning by determining what students will need to know, do and understand, as well as how they can best demonstrate their learning. In developing differentiated instruction, teachers recognise the importance of equity of access to learning opportunities for all students and firmly believe that each student can succeed. This notion referred to as a *growth mindset* advocates that a person's effort, rather than innate ability, is key to academic growth and achievement. It is through continual support and partnership between teacher and student in developing positive attitudes and habits of mind that success can be demonstrated.

A positive learning environment is one that is 'carefully constructed to support each student's need for affirmation, contribution, power, purpose and challenge' (Santangelo & Tomlinson, 2012, p. 314). Teachers can work towards creating a positive learning environment by considering the availability of resources that support and reflect students' diverse backgrounds, sharing responsibility for teaching and learning, providing students with individualised attention, communicating unequivocal respect and concern for each learner, demonstrating cultural competence and using a wide variety of instructional strategies to best meet students' individual needs (Santangelo & Tomlinson, 2012).

Instructional strategies for differentiation

The development of a broad repertoire of teaching strategies suited to differentiated instruction is an important component of becoming an effective teacher of primary science education. During your teaching career, you will likely encounter many different strategies and will need to decide which provide the best fit for your students and their learning needs. Some differentiation strategies serve quite specialised functions, for example, the use of concept maps to enable students to organise their thinking. Other differentiation strategies are more flexible and can be applied in a variety of situations. In the next section, three strategies are highlighted that lend themselves well to primary school science classrooms and might provide a springboard to consideration of additional tools and techniques that will support inclusive classroom practice.

I do, We do, You do

The *I do, We do, You do* strategy involves a gradual release of responsibility from teacher to student and provides a highly scaffolded approach to developing the knowledge, understanding, processes and skills required for students to learn new content and concepts. First, in the *I do* phase, the teacher explicitly informs, explains, models and provides examples. The second phase, *We do*, involves the teacher and students working together in partnership to extend learning. Guided by the models or examples provided by the teacher in the *I do* phase, students are supported through the process of learning new material and move from a listening stance, to actively engaging in practical and cognitive tasks. Group work is an important element of this phase in order to encourage collaborative learning and build the confidence of students who may struggle on their own. The final *You do* phase involves students working individually to apply their knowledge and understanding in practice. It is important that, during this stage, the teacher continues to monitor student progress and provide feedback, support and opportunities for further practice if needed, as noted in Snapshot 10.1.

The type of strategy outlined in Snapshot 10.1 works well in a primary school science classroom where introducing an activity through modelling or a teacher demonstration is a common way of engaging students in the beginning stages of a science lesson or unit of work. Practical science investigations provide natural opportunities for students to work collaboratively in groups and engage in peer-to-peer learning. Scaffolding the initial stages of learning through classroom teacher and peer support provides a supported pathway to independent learning.

Tiered activities

Tiered activities provide opportunities for differentiation by focusing on knowledge, understanding, processes and skills, but at different levels of complexity, abstractness, open-endedness and independence (Tomlinson, 2014). When using tiered instruction, teachers retain the curriculum aligned focus of a learning sequence but make slight adjustments to

SNAPSHOT 10.1: *Year 4 learning about living things*

Ms Turner is aware that her Year 4 students hold a number of alternative conceptions relating to characteristics of living and non-living things. Some of her students classify living things as anything that moves—one student is convinced that fire is a living thing after seeing flames moving on a campfire. Ms Turner believes a series of practical activities will support her students to overcome these misconceptions but realises her students are in the early stages of understanding the nature of scientific investigations and will require structured support.

Ms Turner commences her Term 2 biology unit on Growth and Survival of Living Things by saying to her students 'I planted a seed and it didn't grow! What do you think could be wrong?' This enables her to both establish students' prior knowledge and guide the student discussion towards thinking about how they might plan an inquiry into what living things need to grow. In this *I do* stage, Ms Turner models the initial stages of planning an investigation by *thinking aloud* with her class about the types of things that might need to be considered in setting up a fair test. During this discussion, she guides students towards considering what they will test (independent variable), what they will measure (dependent variable) and what they will need to keep the same in order to ensure the test is fair (controlled variables).

Ms Turner moves into the *We do* stage by working through the completion of a simple investigation planning template as a whole class activity. In subsequent investigations, this level of structure will be gradually reduced so that students are able to move into the *You do* stage and complete a planning template independently. Ms Turner is aware that some students will struggle with this task more than others and so intends to provide ongoing support along with repeated opportunities for practising the skills involved in planning an investigation.

activities and assessment tasks in order to meet the needs of individual students. In practice, the tiering strategy involves the teacher creating different versions of the same task, with scaffolding and support based on the ability levels of students. It is important to make all tiered activities interesting, challenging and reasonable in terms of the expectations placed on students. Activities and assignments can be adjusted in any of the following ways: level of complexity; amount of structure; materials provided; time allowed; pacing of the assignment; number of steps required for completion; form of expression; and level of independence required (New South Wales Department of Education, 2019). In order for this strategy to be successful, it is important for teachers to know their students very well and be cognisant of their prior knowledge and understanding, as indicated in Snapshot 10.2.

Tiered activities are useful in primary school science classrooms, where the teacher might adjust the level of complexity of a particular science investigation, provide greater structure for students who require additional learning support, provide extension activities for gifted and talented learners and look at different modes of assessment for students to demonstrate their learning. Options for varying time to complete the task, and opportunities to work in a group or individually also provide avenues for all students to experience success.

Cooperative learning strategies—jigsaw

A jigsaw is a learning activity that divides students into groups, with each group focusing on a different component of a knowledge set. In setting up a jigsaw activity, the teacher needs to identify the key material that students need to learn and then break this up into manageable chunks of information for students to research and investigate. Students are grouped, usually heterogeneously, and assigned a different part of the material to be learnt. Next, all students with the same learning material come together to form an expert group to discuss, communicate and collaborate with each other until they have successfully mastered the material. They then return to their original home group to teach the material to the others, as the expert. This is exemplified in Snapshot 10.3.

Just as in a jigsaw puzzle, each student's part is essential for full understanding and completion of the activity or task. The cooperative nature of the task encourages the development of *collective mastery* and ensures that every student has an important role to play in achieving the learning goals of the activity. Students who are new to jigsaw learning will require considerable guidance as to what they need to do in order to fulfil their role in their group, and the provision of detailed instructions or handouts can be useful in supporting students to stay on track.

SNAPSHOT 10.2: Year 5 studying the Solar System

Ms Shaw's Year 5 students are studying a unit on the Solar System. Students have participated in an introductory brainstorming session to determine background knowledge and have been shown stories/ videos about the Solar System in order to engage their interest and create a foundation for building further knowledge.

To develop an appropriate tiered activity for the unit, Ms Shaw has consulted her most recent assessment of student learning and considered what she knows about her students' academic abilities, strengths and interests. Based on her understanding of students' needs, she has adapted a previous year research activity on the Solar System by creating a series of versions of the task to match students' ability levels. The differentiated versions of the new tiered activity all contain the same core elements:

- All students will have a mix of individual and group tasks to complete.
- All students will receive some background reading material on the Solar System, appropriately matched to students' reading achievement levels.
- All students will be required to take notes on the material— students who require greater support will be supplied with a scaffold for notetaking.
- All students will be expected to complete Internet-based research to expand their understanding—the teacher will direct students to a variety of websites of differing readability, i.e., some may have simpler text and others may have more complex information to navigate.
- All students will have a variety of avenues to demonstrate their learning (e.g., posters, multimodal presentations, model building).

In designing this tiered activity, Ms Shaw can cater for different levels of ability while ensuring that all students come to know essential key concepts relating to the Solar System and gain valuable process skills such as conducting research and evaluating evidence.

SNAPSHOT 10.3: *Year 6 studying rollercoasters as part of STEM*

In his second year of teaching, Mr Evans is assigned a Year 6 class with a diverse range of abilities, including students with English as a second language, students with diagnosed learning disabilities and a small group of students considered academically advanced, or gifted and talented learners. In order to cater to this diversity, Mr Evans sets about designing a STEM unit that will provide the structure required for those in the class who need higher levels of guided instruction, while providing scope for the more advanced students to be academically challenged and extend their learning. He selects a unit on rollercoasters that will support students to develop an introductory understanding of force and motion, while also developing their skills in technology and design. The task is embedded in an authentic, real-world context, as shown in the following task description:

> You have been hired as a group of engineers for Magic World Theme Park to design their latest rollercoaster, which they require to operate like a marble track. Your task is to research key concepts within the STEM field in order to design your own track. You will then build and test a prototype of your track, before you pitch your design to promote why your design should be chosen.

To commence the unit, Mr Evans implements a jigsaw activity where students are allocated one of four roles: 1. Newtonian physicist, 2. roller-coaster historian, 3. roller-coaster architect and 4. engineer/safety coordinator. Each student is provided with a role description card which provides information about their specific role, along with questions that they need to research and answer in order to successfully complete the task and report back to their group. On completion of the jigsaw activity, students will have developed the background content knowledge required to enable them to begin planning their build of a rollercoaster.

Multidimensional assessment

Multidimensional assessment is an important component of differentiated learning. In the same way that classroom instruction needs to be tailored to individual needs, assessment and the end products of learning should be purposefully designed to enable students to demonstrate their individual strengths and talents. Rather than being a means to a grade-orientated end, assessment tasks should allow students to learn and grow through representing their learning in novel and creative ways. Ideally, effective assessment in differentiated settings will include clearly identified learning goals; meaningful opportunities for cooperative and collaborative learning; scope for varied modes of expression; and appropriate scaffolding and support to ensure that the individual needs of students are accommodated (Santangelo & Tomlinson, 2012).

Regular formative or informal assessment is an important component of differentiated instruction. A pedagogical emphasis on formative assessment can encourage students to embrace challenge and view feedback as a tool for further development rather than an endpoint critique. Encouraging students to keep track of their own skill development, reflect on their strengths and weaknesses and set goals for their future learning are important steps in empowering students to become 'captains of their own fate as learners' (Tomlinson, 2008, p. 30). The use of tools such as portfolios and learning journals are a practical means of providing avenues for students to engage in ongoing self-assessment and self-reflection.

Addressing concerns about differentiation

While the provision of differentiated instruction is a key focus in most schools, many teachers still struggle with the reality of trying to implement differentiated instruction amidst the multiple competing demands on time and energy in the primary school classroom. This can be even more problematic in the case of science education where many primary teachers lack experience or adequate preparation in differentiation. A key point to keep in mind is that differentiation is fundamentally 'student-aware teaching' (Tomlinson, 2008, p. 27). The more you know your students, the more likely you are to experience success in making appropriate adjustments to ensure their success. If you are aware that a student in your science class struggles with reading, you might minimise the reading requirements of a task and instead provide visual or audio prompts in order to remove the reading barrier. Similarly, if you have a struggling writer in your class, speech-to-text assistive technology could allow the student to continue to fully participate in science lessons, while continuing to receive support for writing skill development in other learning sessions. For a gifted student, you might set individual projects or provide extension activities to ensure that they maintain motivation and engagement in their science learning. The key goal here is to ensure that every student has the opportunity to demonstrate their ability to be a critical and creative thinker in the science classroom. Barriers and impediments to learning need to be identified and removed to the best of the classroom teacher's ability. More experienced teachers can often be a source of help and inspiration in relation to making differentiated instruction a practical reality.

Summary of key points

Every classroom you are likely to encounter in a primary school setting will be diverse. Students arrive at school with a wide range of interests, abilities, experiences and cultural and linguistic heritages. Teachers as education professionals are expected to provide an equitable and accessible science education experience for all students. This requires maintaining a positive learning environment where each student is celebrated, respected and supported in their science learning. Beginning teachers are encouraged to know their students well, in order to be able to design learning experiences that account for students' readiness and background knowledge, interests and passions, strengths and weaknesses and preferred modes of learning. Developing a wide repertoire of strategies that support differentiated instruction is an important step in ensuring that diverse learners have equal opportunities to be engaged and active participants in the primary science school classroom.

Discussion questions

10.1. Imagine that you have recently been employed as a teacher at a new school. You discover that you will have a large number of students in your classroom with English as a second language. How will you manage your science classroom to ensure that every student is experienced to position success?

10.2. Choose one instructional strategy from this chapter and describe how you could implement this strategy to teach a key area of science understanding for primary learners, e.g., energy and electricity, our place in space and weather and our environment.

10.3. After engaging with this chapter and reflecting on your own experiences, why do you think it is important to plan for differentiated science lessons in primary school classrooms?

References

Australian Institute for Teaching and School Leadership (AITSL). (2011). *Australian P Standards for Teachers.* Accessed May 31 2020 at: https://www.aitsl.edu.au/docs/default-source/national-policy-framework/australian-professional-standards-for-teachers.pdf?sfvrsn=5800f33c_64.

Australian Curriculum, Assessment and Reporting Authority (ACARA). (2020). *Student diversity.* Accessed May 31 2020 at: https://www.australiancurriculum.edu.au/resources/student-diversity/.

Department of Education and Training. (2018). *National School Reform Agreement.* Accessed June 4 2020 at: https://docs.education.gov.au/documents/national-school-reform-agreement.

Education Council. (2019). *Alice Springs (Mparntwe) Education Declaration.* Accessed June 4 2020 at: http://www.educationcouncil.edu.au/site/DefaultSite/filesystem/documents/Reports%20and%20publications/Alice%20Springs%20(Mparntwe)%20Education%20Declaration.pdf.

New South Wales Department of Education. (2019). *Strategies for differentiation.* Accessed June 10 2020 at: https://education.nsw.gov.au/teaching-and-learning/professional-learning/teacher-quality-and-accreditation/strong-start-great-teachers/refining-practice/differentiating-learning/strategies-for-differentiation.

Santangelo, T., & Tomlinson, C. A. (2012). Teacher educators' perceptions and use of differentiated instruction practices: An exploratory investigation. *Action in Teacher Education, 34*(4), 309–327.

Tomlinson, C. A. (2008). The goals of differentiation. *Educational Leadership, 66*(3), 26–30.

Tomlinson, C. A. (2014). *The differentiated classroom: Responding to the needs of all learners* (2nd ed.). Alexandra, VA: Association for Supervision and Curriculum Development.

PART III

EXTENDING THE ART OF TEACHING PRIMARY SCHOOL SCIENCE TO STEM

11

APPROACHES TO TEACHING STEM IN PRIMARY SCHOOLS

Linda Hobbs and John Cripps Clark

Goals

The goals for this chapter are to support you to:

- Understand what STEM is and how it can be introduced to schools
- Identify different approaches to incorporating STEM in your classroom
- Identify some challenges that you might face when implementing STEM
- Understand some principles for developing and implementing STEM teaching

Australian Professional Standards for Teachers—Graduate Level:

- Standard 2: Know the content and how to teach it (Focus areas 2.1, 2.2)
- Standard 3: Plan for and implement effective teaching and learning (Focus areas 3.1, 3.2, 3.3, 3.4)

Introduction

STEM is an acronym that stands for Science, Technology, Engineering and Mathematics. The term *STEM* is being more frequently used and is stimulating educators to think in new ways about curriculum, teaching and learning. STEM education refers to not only the content of Science, Mathematics and Technologies learning areas but also certain types of thinking, doing and being and is an opportunity for you to put into practice more flexible and productive ways for your students to learn.

There is no single way of talking about what STEM looks like in Australian schools. Many of the teaching strategies used to teach STEM have been around for decades, but they are being revitalised to emphasise authenticity in real-world problems, critical thinking and students taking control over their learning. The *National STEM School Education Strategy* (Education Council, 2016, p. 3) describes 'critical and creative thinking, problem-solving and digital technologies, which are essential in all 21st Century occupations'. Also associated with STEM education is design thinking, entrepreneurship, links with industry and community and the *maker* movement.

There are multiple ways to conceptualise and implement STEM, so you and your colleagues will need to make decisions about what STEM will look like and how to introduce it. As a primary school teacher, you have a degree of flexibility in how you arrange your students' timetable and how you use the space of the classroom and school grounds. As the teacher and member of a teaching team, you will determine how students engage with STEM:

> The vision for Australia must include an education system that expects and achieves a high level of student achievement, mastery, enjoyment and innovation in science, technology and mathematics, year after year—through well-resourced, knowledgeable, inspiring and passionate teams of teachers.
>
> (Prinseley & Johnston, 2015, p. 1)

This chapter begins by discussing different conceptualisations of STEM, then why and how primary schools are introducing STEM. The intention is to provide you with strategies you can use for teaching

STEM, and ways for meeting challenges you may encounter. The chapter provides principles that can guide your planning and implementation of STEM. The aim is that you feel prepared to continue learning how to provide your students with rich and rewarding STEM learning experiences.

What is STEM?

STEM can be conceptualised as the individual STEM disciplines, or an integrated STEM learning experience. It can be a one-off activity or a sequence of lessons. Timms et al. (2018) define STEM as 'the set of disciplines that work together to understand and model the universe so that people can solve problems through harnessing and manipulating the world around them' (p. 20). This description of STEM acknowledges the fact that the different STEM disciplines interconnect and work together. STEM can be conceptualised as disciplinary, cross-disciplinary (also called multidisciplinary or interdisciplinary by some) and transdisciplinary.

A disciplinary approach focuses on the instruction of concepts and skills for one subject, for example, science or mathematics lessons.

A cross-disciplinary approach involves integrating the STEM subjects and includes interdisciplinary and multidisciplinary approaches (Vasquez, 2015). Timms et al. (2018) propose that 'if the concept of STEM is embraced as a meaningful interdisciplinary approach to learning, then schools should be addressing all parts of STEM' (p. 19). The Australian Curriculum, Assessment and Reporting Authority (ACARA, 2016) provides useful examples of how the different learning areas of Science, Mathematics and Technologies can be mapped to portfolios of work labelled as STEM. Cross-disciplinary approaches can be implemented in a number of ways:

- Ideas and concepts from one learning area are used in another learning area. For example, astronomy can be used in a mathematics class as a context for understanding size and scale.
- Ideas learned in one learning area are used to enrich learning in another learning area. For example, learning about the concept of average in mathematics can be applied in a science class, for example, to average the data gathered from an inquiry activity.

- Ideas and concepts and skills from two or more subjects are tightly linked. For example, a STEM unit on designing a solar car incorporates science, mathematics and engineering concepts within the same learning experience.

A transdisciplinary approach refers to a set of practices where knowledge arises at the intersection of multiple disciplines and is promoted as *a way of learning*. This approach often focuses on generic skills rather than an explicit focus on specific content, although disciplinary content must be an important part of this. An example is when students work with real-world problems or design challenges and use knowledge and skills from all disciplines that are needed to solve the problem, sometimes with explicit focus on 21st-century skills such as critical thinking, creativity, collaboration and problem-solving. These skills are also represented by the general capabilities of the Australian Curriculum (ACARA, 2020). An extended example is presented in Chapter 13 on the teaching of environmental sustainability.

Teachers and schools need to have clear goals and a rationale to delineate their specific approach to STEM. Snapshot 11.1 describes the approach that one school is taking for their STEM learning program.

Introducing STEM into schools

There are a number of ways that schools incorporate STEM into an already overcrowded curriculum. STEM teaching and learning may occur within integrated inquiry units of work, within normal classroom teaching, as extracurricular activities or programs (e.g., clubs), as special events (e.g., STEM day) or as specialist classes. In some schools, science specialist roles for teachers are changing to STEM specialists. Some schools have moved towards STEAM (*A* for the Arts). Art allows students to express ideas, especially in the early years, and is a conduit for STEM learning and problem-solving (Gilbert & Borgerding, 2019).

There are three main reasons that schools introduce STEM. Firstly, some primary schools use STEM classes and activities as a way of raising student interest and engagement levels generally, but especially for students who are difficult to engage in more formal learning environments. STEM presents opportunities for less rigid learning contexts as learning tends to be more practical and student-directed, and

SNAPSHOT 11.1: STEM @ the Patch Primary School

The Patch Primary School in Victoria, Australia has a strong STEM program. Their website describes STEM as incorporating both a disciplinary approach to learning the STEM subjects and a cross-disciplinary approach 'that increases student interest in STEM-related fields and improves students' problem-solving and critical analysis skills' (Education Council, 2016, p. 5).

The website details:

- the curriculum links to the Science, Mathematics and Technologies learning areas;
- a rationale for focusing on STEM at the school;
- how STEM is implemented across year levels;
- a process-planning template for STEM that details the steps in planning: inspiration, process, curriculum, supporting knowledge and skills, supporting resources and assessment; and,
- links to a range of resources.

This type of outward-facing demonstration of the school's commitment to STEM education communicates to the broader school community how they want their students to experience STEM and the benefits of that experience. STEM is presented as something that will 'improve student engagement and participation, encourage active learning and address some real-world problems and challenges through an innovative and stimulating STEM education program' (The Patch, n.d., para. 5).

the teacher's role shifts to facilitator of the learning process. STEM can also be used as extension work for gifted and talented students because rich and deep learning can occur through inquiry, designing and problem-solving.

Secondly, some primary schools use STEM as part of their branding to create a competitive edge. Being seen by the community to incorporate STEM shows that the school is being responsive to a changing world and preparing their students for a STEM-rich future.

Thirdly, focusing on STEM allows schools to raise the profile of science and mathematics. A relative drop in Australian students' engagement in science and mathematics and performance in international tests has prompted governments to put more funding into STEM-related programs. Many schools are boosting their science and mathematics programs by introducing STEM activities and thinking.

Approaches to implementing STEM

Part of the attraction of STEM is its versatility. There are a variety of ways of implementing STEM in schools. Four approaches are described below with examples of each. Each approach requires different resources and expertise, produces different outcomes and faces its own implementation issues.

Design challenges

Design challenges can provide an authentic experience of engaging with real-world problems and promote the development of a number of the general capabilities from the Australian Curriculum. Importantly, a critical aspect of the design process is for students to refine and revisit their designs.

Design challenges used in schools may use the technology or engineering design process. There are many versions of the design process, many of which are available online. Interestingly, STEM is enabling engineering to have some prominence in schools even though it is not a separate learning area in the Australian Curriculum. Some great examples of how to bring engineering into the classroom can be found here: https://www. stem.org.uk/engineering-resources/primary.

Engineering and technology organisations will often run design challenges for school students, for example:

- F1 in Schools STEM Challenge (https://www.f1inschools.com/),
- Model Solar Vehicle Challenge (https://www.modelsolar.org.au/),
- Engineers Australia (https://www.engineersaustralia.org.au/ For-Students-And-Educators/Primary-School).

These types of programs provide your students with an engaging and challenging experience, especially as extension activities for more advanced students. Students work in teams to design, construct, test and modify their designs, and to develop resilience, teamwork and problem-solving skills. Prizes and awards can motivate some students, and parents and the community can get involved.

Other examples of design-based projects include:

- *The Covid-19 medical face mask design challenge*, where students consider a current and relevant problem and create a product that will have some social good. Students are challenged to produce a fashionable reusable medical-style face mask. This challenge can be done with pencil and paper but students may use CAD design tools and 3D printers to create prototypes (https://www.datta.vic.edu.au/content/covid-19-face-mask-challenge).
- *Paper planes*, which is a perennial challenge that is particularly engaging in primary schools (http://vmc.global2.vic.edu.au/challenges/paper-planes/).

Students engaging with digital technologies

Some schools focus their STEM programs on digital technologies, particularly robotics and coding. While this isn't the entirety of the Technologies learning area, technologies themselves can be the focus of learning or can be used to solve problems. Digital technologies and *computational thinking* are useful entrées into STEM. There are a wide variety of digital technologies that can be incorporated into your science classroom. It is important to provide your students with the opportunity to engage with new technologies in a playful, social environment with supportive collaboration (Murcia, Campbell & Aranda, 2018). Students will be familiar with computers and tablets, but there is an increasing availability of technology for schools, for example:

- 360° cameras,
- Virtual reality (VR) and augmented reality headsets,
- 3D design programs,
- 3D printers,
- Robotics and digital measuring instruments,
- Bee-Bots and Cubito for younger students,
- Tynker (https://www.tynker.com/),

- MakeCode (https://www.microsoft.com/en-us/makecode),
- Scratch (https://scratch.mit.edu/),
- Hour of code (https://hourofcode.com/au).

Computational thinking is fundamental to coding or programming and refers to the processes we draw on when thinking about how a computer solves problems. It can be done on a screen with either a block or language-based coding; or with tangible objects (robots or blocks) such as Cubito or Bee-Bots. Unplugged programming reduces the need for technology. Students can navigate a map or spell out a name or play a game of snakes and ladders by ordering a sequence of specific instructions on a grid (Aranda & Ferguson, 2018). This is particularly powerful for young children.

Real-world problem-solving

A rich starting point for learning is to start with a problem or scenario from real life, the local community or industry. Linking directly with local industry can be one way of making the problems *authentic*. Problems can range from keeping wildlife off the road and avoiding injury to both drivers and animals; reusing discarded clothing; finding use for mushroom stems that are not wanted by consumers; and programming a robot to help with physiotherapy for children by mimicking the exercises that they need to do.

Problems can also come from within the school. Common school-based problems for students that can have STEM elements include designing elements of the school playground or infrastructure, for example, designing a new sensory garden for students with special needs. Designing a ramp for wheelchair access is the problem presented in Snapshot 11.2.

Extending and integrating STEM into other disciplines

You can give your topics rich and meaningful connections by integrating different disciplines into a STEM unit. You can do this by using historical, geographical or environmental examples. This can be as simple as incorporating the biographies of some of the scientists, mathematicians and technologists that contributed to the topic you are investigating. Snapshot 11.3 describes how the story of Galileo can be used as a rich context for learning about science, technology and mathematics.

SNAPSHOT 11.2: Wheelchair access real-world problem-solving

One activity suitable for senior primary students can be based on a question reported in Hobbs, Cripps Clark and Plant (2018): *What would be the best ramp for wheelchair access to the deck in our garden?*

The initial focus was on mathematics but also had science components:

- Mathematics: What is the best angle for the ramp? What is the area of land it will take up? What volume of concrete will we need to make it?
- Science: How do forces change when the ramp is changed?

The students experimented by:

- measuring a variety of ramps in their local area;
- pushing a wheelbarrow up on ramps of different lengths and angles; and,
- pushing trolleys in their science lessons and measuring the forces needed to push up different ramps.

The students made the following discoveries during this STEM unit. They noticed:

- ramps and structures in the community for people with disabilities;
- connections with people in the community with one girl showing empathy when she noticed people in wheelchairs;
- regulations for ramps and that some of the school ramps failed these regulations;
- why long ramps have horizontal sections midway;
- a need to make decisions about how to record information, how to describe differences between ramps and how to represent the different ramps; and,
- a need for a formula to work out the height if they knew the angle and the length.

SNAPSHOT 11.3: *Galileo's story as a context for STEM learning*

Galileo's story and discoveries are a rich source of scientific, mathematical and technological innovation. In the late 14th century, Galileo Galilei performed a number of experiments to model motion under gravitational forces. He was a skilled musician and worked at a time before the word *scientist* had been coined and as a consequence did not differentiate between mathematics, science, technology or engineering. At that time, he would possibly have been called a *natural philosopher*, and only mathematics was a recognised discipline. One of his many contributions was to realise and eloquently articulate that the physical world is best understood through mathematics. Ways of bringing Galileo's story and discoveries alive in the classroom include the following:

1. Students can read Galileo's dialogue concerning two new sciences (http://galileoandeinstein.physics.virginia.edu/tns_draft/index.html).
2. Many of Galileo's experiments can be replicated, including:
   a. rolling balls down inclined planes. There are detailed lesson plans and workbooks at https://www.resolve.edu.au/modelling-motion; and,
   b. measuring time accurately before modern clocks using water clocks, a pendulum and using a musician to beat time. You can get your students to make the water clocks that measure time accurately (https://teachbesideme.com/homemade-water-clock/).

Galileo did not drop objects from the Leaning Tower of Pisa, but students can debate the historical dispute between the Aristotelian ideas that heavier objects fall more quickly and Galileo's assertion that they fall at the same rate and that any difference was due to air resistance. There is a wealth of material discussing the Pisa story, including Brian Cox's *Galileo's Famous Gravity Experiment* (https://www.youtube.com/watch?v=QyeF-_QPSbk).

Dealing with the challenges of incorporating STEM

Teachers can face a number of challenges when embarking on teaching STEM. Decisions around curriculum are often made by teaching teams or school leaders. However, you have control over your approach to STEM, your own professional learning and how you participate in discussions about what STEM can look like. A common challenge that teachers face is feeling out of their depth because of being unfamiliar with STEM concepts and practices.

Feeling out of my depth

Research shows that primary school teacher graduates often lack confidence in and preparedness to teach mathematics, science and technology (Prinsely & Johnson, 2015). However, take comfort in knowing that your learning does not stop when you leave university and that all teachers will continue learning for their entire career. However, it can take several years for teachers new to teaching a subject to feel confident and capable.

Learning to teach something new needs time, support and an attitude of openness on the part of a teacher and the teaching team. The following may help you to learn to feel comfortable teaching STEM:

- *Become familiar with the different approaches to teaching STEM.* Some of these are outlined above. Consider how new technologies can open up new possibilities for learning through students creating, making and communicating.
- *Use what you already know.* Consider and put to work what you already know and can do, for example, cooking, sewing, woodworking, sports, painting, acting and writing. Any of these areas can become a context for STEM learning when using project-based learning.
- *Find out what your students like to do.* If you are learning, then learn with your students—expect the students to find out things that you were not aware of.
- *Have a go, have a play.* Familiarise yourself with the technology by playing with it, or allow some of your students to have a play.

Principles for implementing STEM in primary schools

When you are planning to introduce a STEM activity, unit or program into your school, there are a number of ideas for you and your colleagues to consider. The following principles have been adapted from Hobbs (2018) to suit the primary school context:

1. Cater for the full education spectrum

    While you are a primary school teacher, it is important to see how the STEM experiences you give your students fit into the context of their educational journey. Some students will go on to work in STEM careers; all will use STEM in their daily lives. It is useful to acknowledge that STEM is taught in early childhood, primary school, secondary school and in tertiary education. Creating a STEM-rich education for students is a shared responsibility.

2. Be deliberate, explicit, practised

    Link subjects and disciplines deliberately by explicitly making connections between the ideas and practices of different subjects for students. This means referring to the disciplines or subjects, teaching explicitly the skills and practices and deliberately teaching the mathematical and scientific concepts that are needed to undertake an inquiry, solve a problem or provide justification for a design. During your initial teacher education, seek every opportunity to practise doing this.

3. Represent STEM in its multiple forms

    Recognise that there is no single way to teach STEM. As discussed above, STEM can be taught as discrete disciplines, through cross-disciplinary approaches or as a transdisciplinary approach that uses an *authentic* context for learning. A school might incorporate any or all of these.

4. Enable through collaboration between groups

    Do not try and do this on your own. Collaboration can open up networks and 'raise an awareness and appreciation of the fact that knowledge is distributed in the education and STEM systems and is accessible if one knows where to look and who to ask' (Hobbs, 2018, p. 229). Other teachers, parents and members of the community have practical skills, knowledge and ideas that will be invaluable.

5. Document, share, communicate

Teachers should record and document what they do, share this with other teachers and communicate the outcomes from their programs. Without this, it is difficult for teachers to know which approaches are most effective, how assessment is used to provide evidence of learning and the types of outcomes that can be expected with the different approaches. These practices are important because they improve student learning, attainment, dispositions, values and aspirations in relation to STEM and the STEM subjects. They also sustain change by embedding new teaching practices and curriculum as a normal part of the school.

Summary of key points

This chapter describes the different ways that STEM is being conceptualised in primary schools. A number of approaches to teaching STEM are described, including design challenges, digital technologies, real-world problem-solving and integrating STEM across subjects. Some advice is provided in the event that you face the challenge of feeling out of your depth when firstly introducing STEM. Also provided are five principles of STEM that can guide your STEM teaching practice and how you collaborate with others.

Discussion questions

11.1. Look at the websites of up to five primary schools in your local area and research their approaches to STEM. What is different about each one? Does the school make clear how their approach to STEM aligns with the curriculum focus or values of the school?

11.2. Make a table of the knowledge and skills that you think would be needed to teach STEM. Tick those you feel confident with and write who could assist you with the rest. Think about your colleagues, parents and community members, your own students and other students in the school, students and teachers from your local secondary schools or tertiary institutions, local council or businesses.

11.3. As you seek employment, you will have to highlight the knowledge and skills you have that would be valued by the school.

What knowledge and skills do you think a school will be looking for in STEM? What experiences, hobbies and expertise do you have that could be used in a STEM classroom?

References

Australian Curriculum, Assessment and Reporting Authority (ACARA). (2020). *General capabilities*. Canberra: ACARA. Accessed July 10 2020 at: https://www.australian-curriculum.edu.au/f-10-curriculum/general-capabilities.

Australian Curriculum, Assessment and Reporting Authority (ACARA) (2016). *STEM connections report*. Accessed July 10 2020 at: https://www.australiancurriculum.edu.au/resources/stem/.

Aranda, G., & Ferguson, J. P. (2018). Unplugged programming: The future of teaching computational thinking? *Pedagogika, 68*(3), 279–292.

Education Council. (2016). *National STEM school education strategy: A comprehensive plan for science, technology, engineering and mathematics education in Australia*. Canberra, Australia: Education Council.

Gilbert, A., & Borgerding, L. (2019). Possibilities and potential with young learners: Making a case for STEAM education. In T. Barbatsas, N. Carr, & G. Cooper (Eds.), *STEM education* (pp. 101–116). Leiden, The Netherlands: Brill.

Hobbs, L. (2018). Epilogue: What now for STEM? In T. Barkatsas, N. Carr, & G. Cooper (Eds.), *STEM education: An emerging field of inquiry* (pp. 221–231). Rotterdam: Sense.

Hobbs, L., Cripps Clark, J., & Plant, B. (2018). Negotiating partnerships in a STEM teacher professional development program: Applying the STEPS interpretive framework. In L. Hobbs, C. Campbell, & M. Jones (Eds.), *School-based partnerships in teacher education: A research informed model for universities, schools and beyond* (pp. 231–246). Dordrecht: Springer.

Murcia, K., Campbell, C., & Aranda, G. (2018). Trends in early childhood education practice and professional learning with digital technologies. *Pedagogika, 68*(3), 249–264.

Prinsley, R. & Johnston, E. (2015). Transforming STEM teaching in Australian primary schools: Everybody's business. Office of the Chief Scientist. Retrieved March 18, 2021 from https://www.chiefscientist.gov.au/sites/default/files/Transforming-STEM-teaching_FINAL.pdf

The Patch, (n.d.). STEM at the Patch Primary School Retrieved Mar 18, 2021 from https://www.thepatchps.vic.edu.au/student-programmes/stem/

Timms, M., Moyle, K., Weldon, P., & Mitchell, P. (2018). *Challenges in STEM learning in Australian schools (policy insights issue no. 7)*. Camberwell: Australian Council for Educational Research (ACER).

Vasquez, J. (2015). Beyond the acronym. *Educational Leadership, 72*(34) 10–15.

12

ENHANCING STUDENT LEARNING THROUGH STEM

Grady Venville and Rachel Sheffield

Goals

The goals for this chapter are to support you to:

- Understand how to enhance learning by focusing on powerful knowledge when teaching STEM
- Use a two-dimensional framework to critique and improve STEM teaching and learning

Australian Professional Standards for Teachers—Graduate Level:

- Standard 1: Know students and how they learn (Focus areas 1.2, 1.3, 1.5)
- Standard 2: Know the content and how to teach it (Focus areas 2.1, 2.6)
- Standard 3: Plan for and implement effective teaching and learning (Focus areas 3.1, 3.3, 3.4)

Introduction: subjects and learning areas

What was your favourite subject at school? Was it biology, or maybe history? Have you ever thought about what *subjects* are and why we have them? Subjects are used to organise and structure the vast amount of knowledge that is taught in schools. Curriculum documents throughout the world are almost all presented as subjects or learning areas that are based on, and often share the name of, an underlying academic discipline, like mathematics or English language. The terms *subject* and *learning area* are often used interchangeably. For example, the Australian Curriculum and the New Zealand Curriculum are both structured into *learning areas*. In contrast, in the US state of California, curriculum documents are structured into *subject areas*, and in the African country of Nigeria, the curriculum is presented as *subjects*. In this chapter, we use the term *learning area* when we refer to the broad areas of knowledge described in the Australian Curriculum. We use the term *subject* more generally to refer to defined areas of knowledge taught in schools. Frequently, a school subject directly correlates with a learning area of the curriculum, but not always.

The letters in the acronym *STEM* stand for the subjects of science, technology, engineering and mathematics. The Australian Curriculum is structured around eight learning areas, including Science, Mathematics and Technologies (Australian Curriculum, Assessment and Reporting Authority [ACARA], 2020). There is no learning area specifically for *engineering*; however, this subject includes concepts and processes that are part of all three learning areas of Science, Mathematics and Technologies and there are content descriptors focussing on engineering principles and systems in the Design and Technologies section of the Technologies learning area (ACARA, 2020).

The purpose of this chapter is to provide you with an understanding of how to ensure students have access to powerful knowledge when you teach STEM. In the next two sections, we explore some theory related to the teaching of STEM, we then introduce a two-dimensional framework that can be used to critique STEM teaching. The chapter finishes with two extended classroom snapshots that you are invited to critique using the two-dimensional framework.

Transdisciplinary STEM vs discipline-based subjects

The term *STEM* is used in this book to refer to the teaching of science, technology, engineering and mathematics subjects in an integrated, rather than separated, way. Chapter 11 describes this as a *transdisciplinary* approach to the curriculum in contrast with a disciplinary approach where science is taught as a separate subject. Instead of organising the planning and the day-to-day school work in a classroom according to the segmented subjects or learning areas of the Australian Curriculum (ACARA, 2020), a teacher using a transdisciplinary STEM approach might select a theme or a problem and draw from the STEM learning areas to help stimulate the students to investigate, explore and learn.

For example, a common discipline-based school subject in science is *Plants and Animals* that focuses on the classification and biology of living organisms. An alternative, transdisciplinary subject is *Endangered Species* that requires students to use biology concepts to understand shrinking habitats, mathematics concepts to extrapolate expected extinction rates and technology concepts to understand artificial propagation of an endangered species. For transdisciplinary STEM subjects, the teacher might select a theme such as *The Yarra River, The Olympics, Human Bodies* or *Our City* and use the different perspectives of the STEM learning areas for the students to study the theme over a four or five-week period. Alternatively, the teacher might select a problem such as *Stopping Sunburn, Dying Fish in the Murray River, Parking Bicycles at School* or *Bugs Eating My Vege Patch*. The teacher would then use the concepts and problem-solving conventions from more than one of the learning areas to enable the students to explore and test solutions to the problem.

The advantage of a transdisciplinary STEM subjects is that knowledge and processes from different disciplines can be used together to solve real-world problems that are interesting to students. Disciplines are bodies of knowledge where academic communities exist to develop and test that knowledge. People in these communities conduct scholarly inquiry to improve our understanding of the concepts and principles related to the discipline. The learning areas of the Australian Curriculum and the subjects taught in schools and universities often reflect related disciplines. The world is a complex place, however, and it is increasingly recognised that we need people with the deep knowledge of different disciplines to come together to solve important problems. For example, the goal of an Australian National University research initiative called Zero Carbon Energy for the Asia Pacific is to develop the knowledge and expertise needed so that Australia can transform its current coal-based energy trade with the Asia Pacific into renewable energy such as solar and wind energy (https://www.anu.edu.au/research/research-initiatives/zero-carbon-energy-for-the-asia-pacific). This project involves physicists, chemists, engineers, social scientists and policy academics all coming together and using their disciplinary expertise to provide and implement solutions to the complex problem of climate change.

The reason we teach STEM is that it is critically important for students to understand the complex world in which we live and the complex problems we face, like climate change. In order to do this, they need to be able to think about issues using knowledge from different disciplines. Research shows that transdisciplinary STEM subjects are often more engaging for students than the study of subjects that are strongly based on one discipline and that with careful planning and excellent teaching, learning also can be enhanced (Rennie, Venville & Wallace, 2012). What students learn and whether it is better for them to study discipline-based subjects or transdisciplinary subjects at school is often debated by educators. In the next section, we discuss the idea of *powerful knowledge* and then present a framework to ensure learning is maximised when teaching transdisciplinary STEM.

Powerful knowledge

Powerful knowledge can be thought of in terms of what knowledge can do or what intellectual power it can give to those who have access to it (Young, 2008). STEM teaching is sometimes criticised as being an unstructured mass of ideas and that students are disadvantaged because they don't learn or practice the concepts and processes from within the disciplines as they might do with a more traditional approach to instruction. This can be a problem as students move through the education system to secondary school where subjects are more focussed on the complex ideas within each learning area of the curriculum. For example, if students do not learn the basics of fractions and multiplication in primary school, they will be unable to understand or apply algebra later. If students are not well prepared to think abstractly about matter being made up of particles while they are in primary school, they will not be able to understand atomic theory in secondary school. In this way, the knowledge that is accessible to students when they study discipline-based subjects is powerful, because it can help them to succeed academically.

Because transdisciplinary subjects are focussed on real-world problems, they can help to enhance students' critical thinking skills such as problem-solving, argumentation, decision-making and conceptualising the same problem from different perspectives and dimensions. These are examples of powerful knowledge because in Young's (2008) terms, they improve a student's intellectual power. As a consequence, we strongly support the teaching of both disciplinary subjects and transdisciplinary STEM subjects; however, we caution that in order to ensure students have access to powerful knowledge, STEM requires careful planning and teaching.

STEM teaching framework for powerful knowledge

To ensure that students benefit from transdisciplinary STEM subjects, Rennie, Venville and Wallace (2020) provided a two-dimensional framework that can be used by teachers to focus their students on powerful knowledge. The first dimension of the STEM curriculum framework is *balance* between transdisciplinary and disciplinary knowledge and the second dimension is *connection* between local and global contexts (Figure 12.1). In the next few paragraphs, we'll expand on what these two dimensions mean in terms of teaching and learning. To illustrate the dimensions of the framework, we'll use the *Bugs Eating My Vege Patch* example of a STEM problem mentioned above.

Balancing transdisciplinary and disciplinary knowledge

The first dimension of the framework acknowledges it is important when considering real-world problems that there needs to be balance between

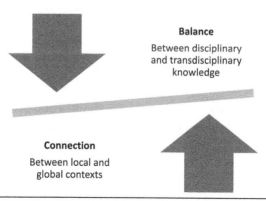

Figure 12.1 The two dimensions of the framework for STEM teaching, balance and connection (based on ideas presented in Rennie, Venville and Wallace, 2020).

the students using both disciplinary and transdisciplinary knowledge. This balance is important because students benefit from understanding the complex real-world transdisciplinary problem; however, they also need to learn and apply the depth of knowledge and the unique conventions and processes that come with the disciplines.

As an example, this balance between transdisciplinary and disciplinary knowledge might be achieved by students initially exploring and describing the problem of insects eating plants in a school or home vegetable garden. To develop a deep understanding of this problem, students will need to be guided by the teacher to use concepts and processes from the relevant disciplines. Students will benefit from developing conceptual understanding as outlined in the Australian Curriculum: Science (ACARA, 2020) about the biology of insects and insect populations. They will benefit from applying problem-solving skills from the Australian Curriculum: Technologies (ACARA, 2020) to test methods of stopping insects getting into a vegetable patch such as using sticky pest strips or companion planting. They could use knowledge learnt in the Australian Curriculum: Mathematics (ACARA, 2020) to estimate the numbers of insects in the vegetable patch and graph their population over time as a way of determining the effectiveness of the methods they used to stop the insects. By using science, technology and mathematics-based knowledge in these in-depth ways, and then putting all of that knowledge together, students will be able to make powerful recommendations about different ways to solve the problem of insects eating the vegetable patch. It is the combination and balance of disciplinary knowledge and transdisciplinary knowledge that makes the learning for the students powerful.

Connecting local and global contexts

The second dimension of the STEM framework is about the *connection* between local and global contexts. Like the first dimension of balance, this dimension is important to support and enhance student learning through the construction of powerful knowledge. We can illustrate this by further considering the *Bugs Eating My Vege Patch* STEM problem. The students may have discovered from their observations that the bugs in their vegetable patch turn out to be caterpillars or the larval form of a moth, such as the cabbage moth (*Mamestra brassicae*). Through further observation and research, students may learn about the body parts and life cycle of the local moth that inhabits their vegetable patch. The teacher may then extend the students to apply what they have learnt to understand the global biological principles of insect body parts and insect life cycles and their relevance to classification. This would result in the connection between the knowledge they have developed about the cabbage moth in their own local garden context and the biological principles about insects, including insect body parts and life cycles that they can apply in contexts globally. This global knowledge can then be applied and tested with other insects that the students might be interested in, thus extending and consolidating their learning. This connection between local and global results in powerful learning. Students are interested and engaged by the local problem, but they benefit from the connected learning to the global biological principles that can be applied across contexts and across time.

The connection between local and global could be further extended with students learning about the worldwide problem of cabbage moths across many countries where agriculture includes the growing of brassica vegetables such as cabbage, broccoli and Brussels sprouts. Moreover, students could experiment using methods to control the moths at the local level, for example, by using a spray-on baking soda and flour mixture, or companion planting of rosemary, and then extend their knowledge by seeking information about how the global agricultural industry controls insects. Further extension might include exploration of the issues caused by the widespread use of insecticides in agriculture.

Analysing powerful learning in STEM

As you implement STEM lessons, topics and projects into your teaching, it is important that you plan for the students to be engaged in powerful learning. The STEM framework of balance and connection is one way to analyse whether the learning for students will result in balanced and connected knowledge. Read Snapshot 12.1 about a primary school teacher, Rahim, who implemented a STEM project for his students on COVID-19 as a result of the global pandemic in 2020. While you are reading the snapshot, think about whether the activities that Rahim implemented balanced disciplinary and transdisciplinary knowledge and connected local and global contexts for his students.

SNAPSHOT 12.1: Year 5 and 6 COVID-19 STEM project

Rahim is a teacher at an inner-city primary school in Canberra. He teaches a combined class of Year 5 and Year 6 students with many high achievers, especially in science and mathematics. Students in Canberra recently had to learn from home for two months during the global COVID-19 pandemic. The students were very interested in the COVID-19 virus, and Rahim decided to use the pandemic as a STEM project that brought together learnings from science, technology and mathematics.

Science learning area: are viruses living or non-living?

From prior observation, Rahim was aware that some of his Year 5 and Year 6 students had trouble understanding what living things are and others had very good awareness of the characteristics of living things. In an early lesson, therefore, he revisited and reinforced the definitions students had previously developed for living and non-living things. Rahim was aware that scientists disagree about whether viruses are living or non-living because they can only reproduce by taking over another living thing's cells and causing them to make more viruses. Rahim's experience as a teacher had given him confidence to challenge his students and give them examples that don't fit with the accepted scientific categories, patterns and rules. Rahim believes this benefits his students because they learn to be critical thinkers. He conducted a Zoom meeting for his class with a virologist from a nearby university. The students planned their questions prior to the meeting and asked, 'Do viruses eat?', 'Do viruses grow?', 'What are viruses made of?', 'How do viruses reproduce?', 'Do viruses have DNA?', and 'What is the difference between the words *Coronavirus* and *COVID-19*?'

After the meeting with the virologist and some further research and discussion, the class agreed that viruses are neither living things nor non-living things, but viruses do a lot of things that are like living things and some of them make humans sick. They agreed that viruses are somewhere in between living and non-living things.

Technologies learning area: evaluating face mask design

Wearing masks during the pandemic was a controversial issue related to both science and sociology in which students in Rahim's class were interested. They discussed the problem and researched the scientific evidence about wearing face masks as it emerged. Rahim provided the students with an opportunity to design and make their own masks to achieve outcomes from the Australian Curriculum: Technologies (ACARA, 2020) part of the COVID-19 STEM project. The students had to conduct research on the requirements for an effective mask and design a mask with parameters, including:

- Three layers of breathable fabric
- 25 cm × 25 cm in size
- Outer layer: Water-resistant fabric like polyester or polypropylene
- Middle layer: Blended fabric like cotton polyester or polypropylene
- Inner layer: Water absorbing cotton fabric

They determined the equipment and skills needed, including:

- Pattern and instructions—available from the ABC website (https://www.abc.net.au/news/2020-07-15/how-do-you-make-a-face-mask-coronavirus-mandatory-buy-melbourne/12454386)
- Sewing machine or hand sewing needle and thimble
- Cotton thread, pins, safety pin
- Fabric—as above
- Elastic for ties
- Scissors, ruler, fabric marker

The students worked with their parents or carers from home to make face masks and showed them to the other students in the class during a Zoom activity. In order for his students to be able to demonstrate the Year 5 and Year 6 achievement standards in the Australian Curriculum: Technologies (ACARA, 2020), Rahim created an activity that allowed them to develop criteria for the success of their face masks and to test and improve the design. Students were asked to talk with members of their family to determine what they would appreciate in the design of a face mask.

Mathematics learning area: understanding the ratio of cases per million

The COVID-19 pandemic and the STEM project was a great opportunity for Rahim to demonstrate to his students how mathematics helps people to understand the world. According to the Australian Curriculum: Mathematics (ACARA, 2020), his Year 5 students had been practicing division by a one-digit number, but most of them could do division by a two-digit number like the Year 6 students. He decided to apply the process of division and the concept of ratio to the STEM project by challenging the students with the question, which country in the world has the worst COVID-19 outbreak? Rahim provided the class with the number of cases of COVID-19 in ten countries, including Australia, as well as the population of those countries on a particular date. He was not surprised when the students in his class disagreed with each other about which country had the worst disease situation depending on whether they took into consideration the population of the country or not. Next, Rahim introduced the concept of cases of COVID-19 per million population. The mathematics process of division and the concept of ratio that his students had been learning and practicing during mathematics were then used to work out the number of cases of COVID-19 per million people in the same ten countries. He asked two capable students to do these calculations using a calculator and then asked them to use Microsoft Excel to create tables and graphs of their new data. Using these tables and graphs, the class then reconsidered the question, which country in the world has the worst COVID-19 outbreak? While the class still did not reach complete agreement, Rahim could see that this exercise had resulted in many of his students thinking differently and he planned to go back to this problem many times during the year until more and more of his students could apply and understand how the ratio improved their interpretation of the data to make a conclusion.

Critique of the Snapshot 12.1

Snapshot 12.1 presents a wonderful example of a primary school teacher who has engaged his students in a complex, real-world problem with direct relevance and interest for them. We can critique the teaching approach using the STEM framework of balance and connection described earlier in the chapter.

The first question is: Did the activities in the COVID-19 STEM project balance transdisciplinary and disciplinary knowledge? Among the three activities in the snapshot, each was related to the COVID-19 pandemic and each one drew on relevant learning areas of the Australian Curriculum (ACARA, 2020). The living things activities drew on the Science learning area, the mask activities drew on the Technologies learning area and the cases per million activities drew on the Mathematics learning area. However, it is apparent that these activities were quite separate and that there was limited transdisciplinary knowledge used by the students. The project implemented by Rahim is probably best described as *multidisciplinary* (Chapter 11). That is, multiple disciplines were used, in this case, they were used to analyse different aspects or concepts that were linked to the COVID-19 topic. Science was used to study the virus itself, technology was used to design the masks and mathematics was used to understand cases per million in the human population. This is not a problem in itself; this was still a terrific multidisciplinary project relevant to students. But Rahim could have enhanced the power of the learning even more if, for example, the mathematics concepts related to size and scale were used to compare viruses with other living things to help them determine if they are living or non-living. He could have incorporated chemistry knowledge and asked the students to design an investigation to test the effectiveness of different mask fabrics for moisture absorption. These activities would have made this project truly transdisciplinary where knowledge from different learning areas intersects. The transdisciplinary approach would have enabled students to build more complex, powerful knowledge, including concepts from the different disciplines, therefore enhancing learning.

The second question is: Did the activities in the COVID-19 project connect local and global contexts? The answer to this question is definitely yes. In particular, the exercises about the number of cases of COVID-19 per million explicitly linked the situation in Australia where the students live to other countries around the world. The connection between the local Australian incidence of the pandemic and global

SNAPSHOT 12.2: Year 2 learning about the Moon

Kyoko has been teaching for five years at a primary school in rural New South Wales. Her Year 2 class is diverse with students from a variety of cultures, including Indigenous Australian students and refugee students. In the Science and Technology K–6 Syllabus (NSW Education Standards Authority [NESA], 2017), Year 1 and Year 2 students are in Stage 1. Kyoko was born in Japan and has a close friend, Misa, who is also a primary school teacher in the Japanese city of Kobe. Kyoko and Misa both love the popular Japanese pastime of Moon viewing, *tsukimi*, and they decided to collaborate on a science and technology project for their Year 2 students to observe, learn and share digital images of the phases of the Moon.

Prior the start of the project, Kyoko had her students draw pictures and tell stories they knew about the Moon. Almost all her students knew that the Moon changes shape and sometimes looks like a circle and sometimes it looks 'like a banana'. When asked why the Moon looks different, students expressed different ideas, for example, some expressed alternative conceptions that clouds cover the Moon and cause the different shapes, or there is a shadow that covers the Moon, others said they don't know. Kyoko asked students if they thought that children all over the world could see the Moon. Two children who had travelled abroad said they saw the Moon when they were in Bali and in New Zealand, but they didn't know if the Moon looked the same as it looks in Australia.

For a whole month, students in Kyoko and Misa's classes in Australia and Japan took a digital photograph of the Moon every day and shared it with each other on a sharepoint site. The students were very excited to see the Moon in the other country. They noticed that sometimes they couldn't see the Moon because of clouds. They noticed that every time they could see the Moon, it looked the same in the other country, except it was curved in a different direction. They noticed that the Moon grew bigger day by day until it was a full circle and then it became smaller day by day until it disappeared. Kyoko taught her students the terms *waxing, waning, full, gibbous* and *crescent*. These activities achieved the Science Skills

Stage 1 outcome that 'A student observes, questions and collects data to communicate and compare ideas' and the Knowledge and Understanding Stage 1 outcome 'A student recognises observable changes occurring in the sky and on the land and identifies Earth's resources' (NESA, 2017, n.p.).

Kyoko taught her students to create a PowerPoint presentation and insert their digital photographs of the Moon from Australia and Japan and play the slide show to demonstrate the changing patterns. They used the new scientific words to label their pictures of the Moon and discussed the patterns they observed. These activities enabled the students to achieve the Digital Systems and Transmission of Data Stage 1 outcome, 'Students recognise that numbers, text, images, sounds, animations and videos are all forms of data when stored or viewed using a digital system' (NESA, 2017, n.p.).

During the month of Moon viewing, Kyoko exposed her students to different cultural stories about the Moon. Misa told the students Japanese stories about the Moon. To develop the cross-curriculum priority of Aboriginal and Torres Strait Islander histories and cultures (NESA, 2017), Kyoko invited a local Aboriginal elder to come to the school to tell her class Indigenous stories about the origin and phases of the Moon. She also asked one of her students' parents to the class to tell Iranian stories about the Moon.

context was very clear. Moreover, the living things activities clearly linked the particular type of Coronavirus that was causing the pandemic with the more global or generic concept of living things that is critical as the basis of biology. Rahim could have enhanced the connection between local and global even more by comparing the cultural norms in Australia and different countries in relation to wearing masks. This also would have enhanced the transdisciplinary aspects of the project by bringing in ideas from the Humanities and Social Sciences learning area of the Australian Curriculum (ACARA, 2020).

Snapshot 12.2 provides you with a different case study of a primary school teacher, Kyoko, who collaborated with a colleague in Japan on a science and technology STEM project on the topic of the Moon for their

Year 2 students. Working with other teachers on STEM curriculum projects often has its challenges, including tension when the collaborators have different ideas and the need for negotiation to work out how things will be done. However, there are many benefits, including learning from colleagues by sharing information and insights. Collaborating on STEM projects also means teachers can discuss and debate teaching strategies with trusted professionals (Sheffield, 2012). Similar to the previous snapshot, while you are reading, think about whether the activities that Kyoko implemented balanced disciplinary and transdisciplinary knowledge and connected local and global contexts for her students.

Critique of Snapshot 12.2

Work with a small group of people in your class, or on your own, to critique Snapshot 12.2 similar to the way we critiqued Snapshot 12.1. Consider the questions: Did the activities in the Moon project balance transdisciplinary and disciplinary knowledge? And, did the activities in the Moon project connect local and global contexts? Think about the teaching that Kyoko did with her Year 2 class and whether it supported the construction of powerful knowledge and about how it could be improved.

Summary of key points

The purpose of this chapter was to provide you with an understanding of how to use a two-dimensional framework to enhance student learning by focussing on powerful knowledge when using a STEM approach. The first dimension promotes the idea that teachers must ensure balance between transdisciplinary and disciplinary knowledge. This will mean students learn the depth of the science, technology, engineering and mathematics disciplines but also are engaged by real-world, complex, transdisciplinary problems and concepts. The second dimension promotes connection between local and global contexts. Teachers engage students in and help them to understand local issues and problems but also to generalise to global contexts and concepts.

Discussion questions

12.1. Some commentators argue that the disciplines were created by human beings to help them better understand the world.

What are disciplines? Are they a body of knowledge, a group of people, a set of conventions and rules or all of these things? What are the similarities and differences between the disciplines of science, technology, engineering and mathematics?

12.2. Consider the science concept of *energy*. Imagine you are teaching a Year 5 class. Look up the Australian Curriculum (ACARA, 2020) and briefly design a four-week STEM project on one form of energy. How will you ensure there is balance between transdisciplinary and disciplinary knowledge and connection between local and global contexts?

12.3. What challenges do you think some students might have when trying to connect local and global contexts? Why? What can you do to support students to make these connections?

References

Australian Curriculum, Assessment and Reporting Authority (ACARA). (2020). *Australian Curriculum*. Accessed May 13 2020 at: https://www.australiancurriculum. edu.au/about-the-australian-curriculum/.

Rennie, L., Venville, G., & Wallace, G. (2020). A worldly perspective: Applying theory to STEM education. In C. C. Johnson, M. Mohr-Schroeder, T. Moore, & L. English (Eds.), *The handbook of research on STEM education* (pp. 39–50). New York, NY: Routledge.

Rennie, L., Venville, G., & Wallace, J. (2012). *Knowledge that counts in a global community: Exploring the contribution of integrated curriculum*. London: Routledge.

Sheffield, R. (2012). Focus on leadership: Constructing a model house at Mossburn School. In L. Rennie, G. Venville, & J. Wallace (Eds.), *Integrating science, technology, engineering, and mathematics* (pp. 88–99). New York, NY: Routledge.

NSW Education Standards Authority (NESA). (2017). *Science and Technology K–6 Syllabus*. Accessed July 20 2020 at: https://educationstandards.nsw.edu.au/wps/portal/ nesa/k-10/learning-areas/science/science-and-technology-k-6-new-syllabus.

Young, M. (2008). From constructivism to realisim in the sociology of the curriculum. In G. J. Kelly, A. Luke, & J. Green (Eds.), *Review of research in education: What counts as knowledge in educational settings* (Vol. 32, 1, pp. 1–28). Thousand Oaks, CA: Sage.

13

AN ECOJUSTICE FRAMEWORK FOR TEACHING ENVIRONMENTAL SUSTAINABILITY AND STEM

Kathryn Paige and David Lloyd

Goals

The goals for this chapter are to support you to:

- plan and implement transdisciplinary STEM learning experiences that have a sustainability focus
- use a range of teaching approaches that promote sustainable practices
- understand the principles of ecojustice and their implications for how we teach
- take an advocate role in the school and local community for attaining sustainable futures

Australian Professional Standards for Teachers—Graduate Level:

- Standard 2. Know the content and how to teach it (Focus areas 2.2, 2.3, 2.4)
- Standard 3. Plan for and implement effective teaching and learning (Focus areas 3.1, 3.2, 3.3)

Introduction

"'We'll all be rooned", said Hanrahan', reflecting on drought and floods. This was written by Australian bush poet John O'Brien (2007) in 1921. Last summer brought Australia catastrophic bush fires, drought, COVID-19 and flooding rains. Some of this was natural; much of it was a result of human-induced climate change, overpopulation and overconsumption. As Australians we understand that we live on ancient soils that have been cared for by Indigenous peoples for tens of thousands of years. However, some of us have lost our connection to place as a result of many factors, including a focus on the economy and the promotion of growth and development. We are at a critical stage of planetary health. The warning signs are loud and clear that humans are responsible for much of the destruction of fresh air, clean water and healthy soil. Things need to change. This view is shared by world-famous environmentalist David Suzuki, who recently asked:

> Can we relearn what humanity has known since our very beginnings—that we live in a complex web of relationships in which our very survival and well-being depend upon clean air, water, soil, sunlight (for photosynthesis) and the diversity of species of plants and animals that we share this planet with?
>
> (Suzuki, 2020)

What can we do in the classroom so that there is a flourishing future for the next generation of students? This chapter sets out to address this question by introducing a set of ecojustice principles as a framework for planning your teaching and learning. The chapter provides several practical examples of how to use the framework to draw on a transdisciplinary STEM curriculum to teach environmental sustainability. In this chapter, we use the term transdisciplinary STEM to acknowledge that the disciplines of science, technology, engineering and mathematics interconnect and work together in real-world environmental contexts (see Chapter 11). Environmental sustainability is a transdisciplinary problem. Therefore, a STEM curriculum is essential for students to understand the problem and potential solutions. The examples of using the ecojustice framework to teach environmental sustainability provided in the following sections include environmental pledges, citizen science, a place-based approach,

Indigenous perspectives, random acts of gardening and native bees in community gardens.

Ecojustice principles: a framework for teaching environmental sustainability

Education of our students can contribute to ecojustice learning by introducing, and making explicit, the necessity of valuing all aspects of Earth systems (Ferreira, Ryan & Davies, 2015). As a beginning teacher of science, you can choose to focus on ecojustice and its application to the places in which we live. You are in a position to awaken your students' awareness and call them to action to nurture healthy, resilient communities and ecosystems.

A set of ecojustice principles, collaboratively developed by Paige, Lloyd and Smith (2019), provide a coherent approach to learning and teaching in primary school classrooms. The principles reflect what we believe all societies must move towards to achieve sustainable human living and the welfare of all species. Table 13.1 lists the ecojustice principles and provides examples of practice, some of which will be explored next. All of the experiences described are excellent starting points to introduce ecological sustainability into primary classrooms.

The ecojustice principles focus on enhancing socially and ecologically just communities. They challenge assumptions around growth and development and promote valuing natural and human systems, knowing our place, developing a respect for possible futures, being culturally responsive and taking an activist role, all of which are equally relevant to providing a sustainability dimension to teaching science. The next section provides descriptions of practical examples of how these principles have been implemented in educational settings.

Examples of using the ecojustice framework

Environmental pledges

The aim of environmental pledges is for either an individual, a class or both to select an aspect of their life at home or school where they can make some reduction in resource use or reduction of harm to the environment. This practice links in particular to ecojustice principle 3. Recording responses to the questions 'What is the personal action you are looking at undertaking?' and 'What data will you collect to measure the effect of

Table 13.1 Ecojustice principles and practices

Ecojustice education principles	Examples of practice and action
1. Identify and challenge current world views and behaviours	Promote the reattachment of humans to Earth Recognise our ecological footprint (water, energy, food, clothing etc.) Reduce waste Study and support native Australian bees
2. Develop a community of learners with a disposition to knowing and valuing with compassion natural systems, including human systems	Act in the interests of all Earth citizens, humans and other-than-humans Look after local environments such as wetlands and river systems Boundary crossing, e.g., school and community collaboration on community gardens and local native environments
3. Invite students to engage collaboratively in working towards creating socially and ecologically just and sustainable communities	Place-based experiences such as volunteering for *Trees for Life*, participating in community gardens and managing common ground Place-based transdisciplinary units Environmental pledges Include all aspects of knowing, feeling and doing
4. Assist students to become role models who value the commons, partnerships, quality of life, creativity and material adequacy	Observational drawing, environmental sculptures Visit/take part in environmentally connected businesses/institutions Manage school and community recycling Activist role in school and community engagement
5. Promote students' acquisition of eco-social wisdom—ways of thinking, feeling and acting within the places they inhabit	Citizen science projects, random acts of gardening Spend time in the natural world with humans and other-than-humans Rewilding: using senses
6. Help students to develop a respect for long-term rather than short-term thinking through historical and futures studies	Historical studies of the places we live Futures scenarios to explore possible, probable and preferred futures Transdisciplinary learning and acting
7. Provide opportunities for students to reflect critically on what they have learnt	Slow pedagogy: promoting connectedness to the environment Plan, enact and engage knowledges, including Indigenous narratives
8. Prioritise culturally responsive pedagogy and Indigenous perspectives	Plan for a long-term view of building relationships and trust with communities, allowing Indigenous communities and Elders to share their knowledge and narratives of local histories and environments on their own terms Learn in local places Read Bruce Pascoe Learn about local Indigenous calendars that order seasons and engage with nature, including a cosmology

your changed action?' encourages a commitment to making a change. Calculating the improvement over time incorporates a numeracy lens to enable a transdisciplinary STEM curriculum, for example:

- How many litres of water have we saved?
- How much less waste is in the landfill bin?
- How much less paper have we used in the school?

One preservice teacher on placement implemented a sustainability pledge using a Teaspoon of Change (small action × lots of people = big change) (https://teaspoonsofchange.org/) from the United Nations Global Goals for Sustainable Development.

Two other examples that early career teachers have incorporated in their classroom are described in Snapshots 13.1 and 13.2.

SNAPSHOT 13.1: *A class pledge to save water*

In a Year 2 science unit on Earth's resources (water), the class pledge was to save water. The students focused on turning off the tap when brushing teeth and then calculated brushing teeth for 2 minutes twice a day (4 minutes total) with tap off. This would save approximately 36 L each per day—based on approximately 9 L/minute from the tap. Over 31 days, each student saved 1116 L and the class saved 30,132 L (26 children and me). All were proud of themselves. (Early Career Teacher 1)

SNAPSHOT 13.2: *Wipe out waste*

The primary school classes in my school have taken on the Wipe Out Waste programme. The Student Representative Council set up recycling bins for 10c containers and started a composting system for food scraps. This was promoted in my class and we try to set an example. Science involves studying plants and we have our own vegetable garden. I hope it gives students the skills and knowledge to create their own (Early Career Teacher 2).

Citizen science

Citizen science involves professional researchers engaging the public to collect data. Citizen science projects can engage students in transdisciplinary STEM with a focus on environmental sustainability. There are many examples of citizen science projects, for example, Operation Spider in 2010 described in Snapshot 13.3. Each project runs for a month or so with citizens/students collecting data about the animals being studied and uploading photographs taken to a website for urban ecologists to collate and add to science understanding. There are also Australian and international examples such as the Atlas of Living Australia for tracking birds and animals in backyards (https://inaturalist.ala.org.au) and the Citizen Science Global Partnership (https://ecsa.citizen-science.net/blog/citizen-science-global-partnership).

Two preservice teachers undertaking their final placement in the same school had the opportunity to team teach a Year 4/5 class one day a week. Their mentor teachers suggested that they select a theme for each day which provided the opportunity to teach a citizen science topic around spiders. After researching background information about spiders, they planned and implemented a sequence of engaging and interactive learning experiences. Pre- and post-drawings provided an opportunity to assess their students' learning about physical characteristics of spiders. Students' questions were gathered and investigated. The preservice teachers describe and reflect in Snapshot 13.3.

There is a growing understanding of the benefits of citizen science, including the benefits to scientists to community participants and students who benefit from skills development and changes to attitudes and behaviours. In addition, teachers and students can engage with and learn from real data. This practice links in particular to ecojustice principles 4, 5 and 7.

A place-based approach

A place-based approach to learning connects students to place, draws on more than one traditional discipline and incorporates Indigenous perspectives with the aim of coming to a deeper understanding of current issues and problems (Paige, Lloyd & Smith, 2019). Snapshot 13.4 provides an example of a place-based transdisciplinary STEM unit of work with a focus on local indigenous plants. Snapshot 13.5 provides an

SNAPSHOT 13.3: *Operation Spider*

Engagement/before views. We introduced the students to Operation Spider and citizen science by giving them some play dough and pipe cleaners for them to show us what they think a spider looks like. They then drew and labelled their spider in their science books. These two hands-on activities gave us an insight into their knowledge of spiders. We noticed that there were many different views: some model spiders had six legs while most had eight; some had lots of tiny holes for eyes, others two eyes; some had two body parts, others only had one.

Explore/explain activities. We set the classroom up into five workstations: each station had a poster which outlined the exploratory activity and a list of questions for students. The spiders in the perspex provided an opportunity for the students to develop their conceptual understanding of physical characteristics of spiders by viewing real spiders safely. They were asked to name a spider, count its legs, describe the colours/patterns that it had, list any interesting features and sketch the spider. The microscopes allowed the students to get a closer look at the detail of each spider, including the hair on its body. Students were also given the opportunity to explore the schoolyard for spiders.

Elaborate/evaluate. We made a spider web by passing a piece of string around. As each student passed the string to a different person, they asked a question. The questions were written onto a brightly coloured cut-out spider and glued to the giant web. Some questions included: What is their web made of? Which spiders are poisonous? How many legs do spiders have? How do they make their webs? Where do they live? How many species are there in Australia? We reviewed our plasticine spiders and asked questions, 'What would you change on this spider?' After lunch, we played several short videos about spiders narrated by David Attenborough. The students were so fascinated by this, they absolutely loved the videos.

SNAPSHOT 13.4: Exploring local indigenous plants

Exploring indigenous Plants is an example of a transdisciplinary STEM unit of work using scientific, mathematical and sustainability lenses. The aim is to develop students' sense of belonging to place, which is important as primary school students are more likely to look after something they are connected to.

This unit could begin by locating indigenous plants in the school grounds and developing connection to place through using all of the senses: smell (e.g., describing smells associated with their plant), touch (e.g., does it matter which part of your body you use to touch?), texture (e.g., using crayons and paper to make rubbings of woody stems, dead leaves) and sound (e.g., finding a space near the tree, sitting quietly and listening for a range of sounds, recording an aural map). A significant tree is then selected and, by visiting regularly over several weeks, small changes in the tree and its environment are observed.

The key science concept is environmental interdependence, in particular, between the tree and animals. The science lens can involve investigating the properties of soil such as colour, pH and porosity and identifying invertebrates living in the soil. The science lens also can incorporate investigating the weather, including estimating, measuring and recording the temperature, humidity and percentage cloud cover. Measuring weather also includes learning and applying mathematics concepts and skills, and hence, students will also achieve mathematics outcomes. This lens can also involve estimating the number of leaves, nuts or fruits on the tree, the diameter of the trunk and the surface area of shade at different times of the day.

The sustainability lens can be used to explore questions such as: What was this place like before the school was built? What species of plants and animals were there? What materials in this place could have been used for tools, games, food and toys? Students can be encouraged and supported to take action, including planting indigenous sedges and grasses to encourage butterflies and bees on the school grounds.

SNAPSHOT 13.5: *Local wetland*

A place-based transdisciplinary STEM unit of work was collaboratively developed by a group of Year 5 teachers who were investigating an aspect of their pedagogy within the chosen topic of fresh water. One key aspect of the pedagogy was sustained classroom time spent in the local wetland. Whole days were allocated on a weekly basis over one or two terms. During this phase, the teachers provided scope for students to explore their own questions relating to their local body of water, including: How do purple swamp hens stand on the reeds? How do birds make their nest in the water? Can dirty water be cleaned? These questions were explored through learning experiences such as: students' chosen investigations about water, observation walks to the wetlands, research using the Internet and books and participating in citizen science projects. Teachers introduced concepts from the STEM disciplines to connect students to their place. The science aspects of the unit of work focused primarily on ecology, identification of macroinvertebrates and measuring water quality, including salinity and acidity. The mathematics included data collection about local species, scaled measurements and calculating the mass of sandbags. Disciplines outside STEM also were incorporated, for example, a history lens was used to understand the history of local flooding and the development of urban artificial wetlands (http://www.waterliteracies.org.au/).

---

example of a place-based transdisciplinary STEM unit of work with a focus on a local wetland. Place-based teaching practices link in particular to ecojustice principles 2, 3, 6 and 8.

The incorporation of citizen science projects involved students collecting, recording and uploading data on water quality, monitoring birds through observation and drawing and collecting feathers to contribute to a feather-mapping project. Rubbish was collected regularly then analysed and the results were communicated to the school and wider community. Of particular importance is that the teachers ensured an explicit focus on the mathematics and science learning throughout the project. This snapshot links to ecojustice principles 2, 3, 6 and 8.

Using Indigenous perspectives

During the first three years of our teacher education program, preservice teachers engage with Aboriginal and Torres Strait Islander histories, knowledges and perspectives. This work prepares them to incorporate Aboriginal and Torres Strait Islander histories and cultures in classroom practice. As a teacher, you can help your students address this cross-curriculum priority by engaging with literature by Indigenous authors and with local community narratives and experiences through written texts, film and digital media as well as working with Elders and community members (O'Keeffe, Paige & Osborne, 2019). School students can be introduced to Aboriginal ways of knowing within the context of place-based learning. For example, students can learn about local calendars that order seasons and nature, as well as Australian Indigenous cosmology. Students can also visit sites of natural and cultural significance to Indigenous people in their local community.

There are many valuable resources regularly being produced and this allows teachers to be responsive to social, cultural and justice-related concerns as they arise in the community and the media. Examples include *Young Dark Emu* (Pascoe, 2019), a documentary film *In My Blood It Runs* (https://inmyblooditruns.com/), as well as a range of web-based resources (https://www.indigenous.gov.au/teaching-guides/curricula-project). This practice links to ecojustice principles 2, 5 and 8 as well as strengthening student engagement with the cross-curriculum priority of Aboriginal and Torres Strait Islander Histories and Cultures.

Random acts of gardening

Finding a place in the school locale that needs greening is an exciting and environmentally proactive way to end a term. After selecting an appropriate location, and gathering a collection of plants, equipment, compost and watering cans, planting is undertaken. This planting can be done with permission from the principal or the owner of the location. It is a collegial act of green that is appreciated for months to come by everyone walking past. There is a sense of fun and achievement, and a sense that the students can make a direct difference. It is a small act, but a powerful one. In *Seeds of Hope*, Jane Goodall (2014) writes about random acts of gardening as a way to brighten dreary neighbourhoods, and Richard Reynolds provides many examples of guerrilla gardening (http://www.

guerrillagardening.org/) (Paige, Lloyd & Smith, 2019). This practice links in particular to ecojustice principles 2, 3, 6 and 8.

Australian bees and community gardens

Concern for the plight of the honeybee, which has experienced colony collapse in the United States and Europe likely caused by human activity, has prompted Australian scientists to promote the importance of bees indigenous to the Australian continent. Species in South Australia are solitary and therefore not affected by colony collapse. Snapshot 13.6 describes a unit of work on Australian bees for Year 1 and 2 students.

SNAPSHOT 13.6: Year 1 and 2 students studying Australian bees

A Year 1and 2 combined class went on weekly excursions to the Old School Community Garden. They began by growing vegetables, which were taken back to school for cooking and eating. Students were encouraged to observe the insects they saw and to identify those they believed to be bees—the blue-banded bee was the easiest to find due to its size and colouring, but students also got to see other native bees and the hive bee, which is the most common in the garden. They researched native bees with the help of their teacher and built bee hotels (bundles of small hollow plant stems such as bamboo). As a result of this activity, the students came to a better understanding that there are many different kinds of bees and that they are an essential part of our ecology for pollination, not only for garden and agricultural plants, but also plants that live in the undeveloped environment. These activities, together with the research students completed at school, enabled them to promote the value of Australian bees with their family and friends. Their work assisted the community to better understand their local ecology, contributing to their personal well-being and encouraging actions that contribute to the health of the local environment. A primary value of this work is connecting to place and understanding that human beings are integrally connected to the ecosystems in which they live and that we have a responsibility to act wisely. This practice links in particular to ecojustice principles 1, 2, 3, 4, 5, 7 and 8.

Summary of key points

There is much evidence to support the idea that human beings have to change the way they live, to reduce their ecological footprint and reconnect with the natural world. We suggest that teachers are in a position to work with young people to be part of this change. We ask you to be brave and adventurous with a transdisciplinary STEM curriculum, focus on environmental sustainability and provide rich experiences that promote activism and incorporate ecojustice principles.

The ecojustice principles provide a way into science and environmental learning that draws upon and develops STEM learning. The principles provide a structure for planning, teaching and assessing students' learning and assist students to get to know the nature and value of the places in which they live. The transdisciplinary approach to learning in familiar places can connect students cognitively, affectively and spiritually to their living place and places they visit. The learning is invaluable for assisting students to contribute as citizens to their communities and for furthering their education.

Discussion questions

13.1. How would instigating an environmental pledge work at an individual and a class level? List three specific examples of environmental pledges and describe what impact each pledge would have if applied by an individual and a whole class? What is the difference?

13.2. Explore websites of environmental organisations and movements such as *Planet Ark, Sea Shepherd Australia, United Nations World Environment Day, Greenpeace* or the *Butterfly Conservation Council*. How could these websites be used in a primary school classroom? How would you ensure that, rather than passive observation, students actively develop or apply knowledge by using these websites?

13.3. Aboriginal and Torres Strait Islanders Histories and Cultures is one of the three cross-curriculum priorities of the Australian Curriculum (ACARA, 2020). Consider the paper by O'Keeffe, Paige and Osborne (2019) listed in the references on preservice teachers' confidence and knowledge of Aboriginal culture. What steps can you take now to ensure that you are well prepared to engage your students in 'reconciliation, respect and recognition of the world's oldest living continuous cultures' (ACARA, 2020, n.p.)?

References

Australian Curriculum, Assessment and Reporting Authority (ACARA). (2020). Accessed Mar18, 2021 at: https://www.australiancurriculum.edu.au/about-the-australian-curriculum/.

Ferreira, J., Ryan, L., & Davies, J. (2015). Developing knowledge and leadership in pre-service teacher education systems. *Australian Journal of Environmental Education, 31*(2), 194–207.

Goodall, J. (2014). *Seeds of hope: Wisdom and wonder from the world of plants.* New York, NY: Grand Central Publishing.

O'Brien, J. (2007). *Around the boree log and the parish of St Mel's.* Sydney, NSW: Harper-Collins Publishers Australia.

O'Keeffe, L., Paige, K., & Osborne, S. (2019). Getting started: Exploring pre-service teachers' confidence and knowledge of Aboriginal culture. *Asia-Pacific Journal of Teacher Education, 47*(2), 152–175.

Paige, K., Lloyd, D., & Smith, R. (2019). *Intergenerational education for adolescents toward liveable futures.* Newcastle upon Tyne, UK: Cambridge Scholars.

Pascoe, B. (2019). *Young dark emu: A truer history.* Broome, Western Australia: Magabala Books Aboriginal Corporation.

Suzuki, D. (2020). *The COVID-19 pandemic may be an opportunity to transform the way we live.* Accessed 27 March 2020 at: https://www.cbc.ca/documentaries/the-nature-of-things/the-covid-19-pandemic-may-be-an-opportunity-to-transform-the-way-we-live-1.5512241.

INDEX

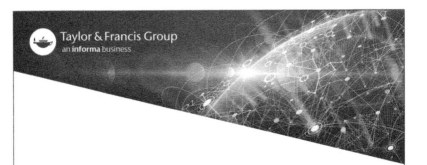

—